Michelson and the Speed of Light

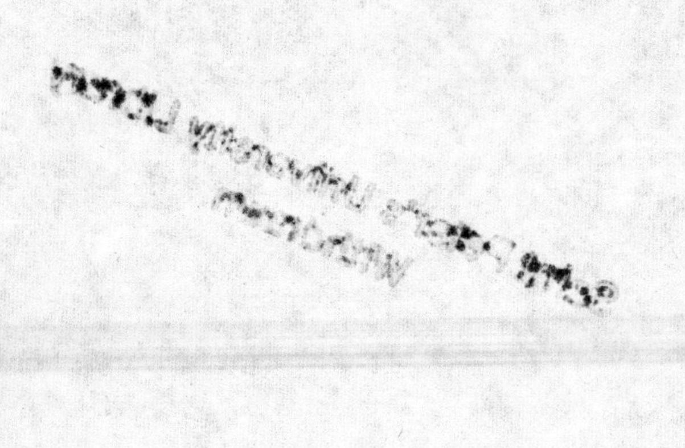

BERNARD JAFFE was born in New York in 1896 and was educated in the public schools of New York City, at City College (B.S.) and Columbia University (M.A.). Author of both textbooks and popular science books, including *Crucibles, the Story of Chemistry; Men of Science in America;* and *Chemistry Creates a New World,* he has written as well for the *New York Times Magazine, Saturday Review, Reader's Digest, School Science and Mathematics,* and several encyclopedias. His books have been translated into many foreign languages. Mr. Jaffe, who is a member of the History of Science Society, the American Chemical Society, and Phi Beta Kappa, recently retired from active teaching and lecturing and now devotes all of his working time to science writing and consulting.

Of the teaching of physics and, in particular, his choice of Michelson for this book, he writes: "I believe there is a widespread desire by people of all ages for a simple, basic understanding of the various sciences and their major achievements. I believe, too, that the lives of the great scientists offer inspiration and motivation for further study. And I am convinced that science can and should be taught as the humanities—not as a collection of facts, but as a product of human thought, experimentation, and imagination. Michelson appealed to me as an unusual figure and a great pioneer. He was an immigrant of humble birth who rose to become America's first Nobel laureate in science. His work on the speed of light, and the ether drift experiment which banished the notion of the ether, are classics of science, and as such should be known to every student of physics."

Other Books by Bernard Jaffe

Crucibles, the Story of Chemistry
Outposts of Science
Men of Science in America
Chemistry Creates a New World
New World of Chemistry
Chemical Calculations
New World of Science (co-author)
Laboratory and Workbook Units in Chemistry (co-author)

Michelson and The Speed of Light

Bernard Jaffe

Published by Anchor Books
Doubleday & Company, Inc.
Garden City, New York

ILLUSTRATIONS BY R. PAUL LARKIN

Library of Congress Catalog Card Number 60–13533

Printed in the United States of America

ONCE MORE TO
CELE

Desist from thrusting out reasoning from your mind because of its disconcerting novelty. Weigh it, rather, with discerning judgment. Then, if it seems to you true, give in. If it is false, gird yourself to oppose it.

LUCRETIUS (96–55 B.C.)

The light dove, piercing in her easy flight the air and perceiving its resistance, imagines that flight would be easier in empty space.

IMMANUEL KANT (1724–1804)

THE SCIENCE STUDY SERIES

The Science Study Series offers to students and to the general public the writing of distinguished authors on the most stirring and fundamental topics of physics, from the smallest known particles to the whole universe. Some of the books tell of the role of physics in the world of man, his technology and civilization. Others are biographical in nature, telling the fascinating stories of the great discoverers and their discoveries. All the authors have been selected both for expertness in the fields they discuss and for ability to communicate their special knowledge and their own views in an interesting way. The primary purpose of these books is to provide a survey of physics within the grasp of the young student or the layman. Many of the books, it is hoped, will encourage the reader to make his own investigations of natural phenomena.

These books are published as part of a fresh approach to the teaching and study of physics. At the Massachusetts Institute of Technology during 1956 a group of physicists, high school teachers, journalists, apparatus designers, film producers, and other specialists organized the Physical Science Study Committee, now operating as a part of Educational Services Incorporated, Watertown, Massachusetts. They pooled their knowledge and experience toward the design and creation of aids to the learning of physics. Initially their effort was supported by the National Science Foundation, which has continued to aid the program. The Ford Foundation, the Fund for the Advancement of Education, and the Alfred P. Sloan Foundation have also given support. The Committee is creating a textbook, an extensive film series, a laboratory guide, especially designed apparatus, and a teacher's source book for a new integrated secondary school physics program which is undergoing continuous evaluation with secondary school teachers.

CONTENTS

Michelson and the Speed of Light

CHAPTER I

An Ensign Clocks the Speed of Light

In the spring of 1879 the New York *Times* said, "The scientific world of America is destined to be adorned with a new and brilliant name. Ensign Albert A. Michelson, a graduate of Annapolis, not yet twenty-seven years old, is distinguishing himself by studies in the science of optics in measuring the speed of light." The New York *Daily Tribune*, in a column headed "Science for the People," described Michelson's experiment. 'Way out in Nevada, the local paper of the mining town of Virginia City proudly announced, "Ensign Albert A. Michelson, a son of Samuel Michelson, the dry goods merchant of this city, has aroused the attention of the whole country by his remarkable discoveries in measuring the velocity of light."

Although the speed of light had been the subject of much thought and discussion since ancient times, only three scientists, all Frenchmen, had succeeded in clocking it with purely terrestrial methods. It was a very old and a very complicated problem. Until Michelson came along, no one in all the Americas had even attempted the difficult experiment.

But over the centuries philosophers and scientists had accumulated considerable information about light's properties. As long ago as 300 B.C., when Euclid was writing his geometry, his fellow Greeks had subjected light to some mathematical investigation. It was known that light traveled in straight lines, and that when light is reflected from a plane mirror, the angle of incidence at which it meets the mirror is equal to the angle of reflection at which it leaves the mirror. The ancients were familiar with the refraction of light. This phenomenon is the change of direction light takes when it passes from one medium, such as air, into another medium of different density, such as water. Claudius Ptolemy, the Alexandrian astronomer and mathematician, compiled tables of measured angles of incidence and refraction, but the law of refraction was not discovered until 1621, when the Dutch mathematician Willebrord Snell, of Leyden, discovered that the ratio of the sines of the angles of incidence and refraction is a constant for the same two media of different densities.

Speculation about the cause of rainbows occupied many ancient philosophers, including the great Aristotle and the Roman statesman Lucius Seneca. Aristotle thought that reflection of light from droplets of water caused the variation of color, and Seneca, similarly, regarded moist clouds as a kind of mirror. In one form or another—myth, legend, philosophical debate, or observation—man has exhibited his curiosity about light through all recorded history.

Like most of the ancients (Empedocles was an exception), Aristotle believed that the speed of light was infinite. It would have been remarkable if he had thought otherwise. No method or instrument within his reach could possibly have measured so great a velocity. But over the centuries his successors continued to ponder the matter and to argue about it. Some 900 years ago the Islamic scientist Avicenna reasoned that the speed of light, while very fast, must be finite, and one of his contemporaries, the Arabian physicist Alhazen, who was the first to explain twilight, agreed. Neither, of course, had any experimental data whatever to support his contention.

GALILEO'S LIGHT EXPERIMENT

Such discussion could have rambled on until doomsday. What was needed was a hard, definitive experiment to produce an answer. The first to propose such an approach was the versatile Italian genius Galileo Galilei. He suggested that two men be stationed on hilltops several miles apart and that they flash signals with lanterns equipped with shutters. His proposed experiment, which scientists of the Florentine Academy subsequently did try, appears in his *Dialogues Concerning Two World Sciences* (published in Leyden, in 1638).

In Galileo's book there are three interlocutors. One of them, Sagredo, asks, "Is light instantaneous or momentary or does it, like other motions, require time? Can we decide this by experiment?" Simplicio, an Aristotelian, is quick to answer, "Everyday experience shows that the propagation of light is instantaneous," and he gives as evidence the "instantaneous" flash of artillery fired at great distances. Sagredo shrewdly counters, "The only thing I am able to infer from this familiar bit of experience is that sound travels more slowly than light."

Then Salviati (who expresses Galileo's opinions) cuts in. "I have devised a method which might accurately ascertain whether the propagation of light is really instantaneous. Let each of two persons take a light contained in a lantern, such that by the interposition of the hand, the one can shut off or admit the light to the vision of the other. . . . In fact, I have tried the experiment only at a short distance, less than a mile, from which I have not been able to ascertain with certainty whether the appearance of the opposition light was instant or not, but if not instant, it is extraordinarily rapid."

With the tools available in his day Galileo, of course, could not have settled the problem so easily, and he realized it. The controversy continued. Robert Boyle, the celebrated Irish scientist who gave chemistry its first true definition of a chemical element, held the speed of light to be finite, but another seventeenth-century genius, Robert Hooke, considered the velocity too great for experimental determination. Johannes Kepler, the astronomer, and René Descartes, the mathematician, went along with Aristotle.

ROEMER AND A MOON OF JUPITER

In 1676 there came a breakthrough. It happened in a roundabout way, more or less by accident. The theoretical problem was solved in pursuit of an entirely practical project, an occurrence not rare in the history of science. Because of expanding trade and the increasing importance of navigation, the French Royal Academy of Science was seeking better maps, and specifically an accurate way to determine longitude. Now, determining longitude is simply a matter of knowing the difference of time at two places, but the clocks of the day were not sufficiently accurate. It was thought that some celestial event occurring daily at the same instant could serve as reference for both the time at Paris and the time aboard ship. The navigator at sea or the geographer on an exploring trip could observe the event, set his own clock, and know the exact time in Paris. Such an event, visible everywhere on land or at sea, is the eclipse of one of Jupiter's four large moons, discovered in 1609 by Galileo.

Among the scientists engaged for the undertaking was a young Danish astronomical assistant named Ole Roemer. The French astronomer Jean Picard had brought him to Paris four years earlier to work at a recently completed observatory. Like the other astronomers of his day, Roemer knew that the period between successive eclipses of Jupiter's innermost satellite varied in the course of the year; the maximum time difference between observations taken six months apart at the same place on earth was about 1320 seconds. The time delays puzzled the observatory men, and all attempts to explain the 1320 seconds had failed to convince. The period of revolution of the satellite seemed to be related to the position of the earth in its orbit with respect to Jupiter. Roemer,

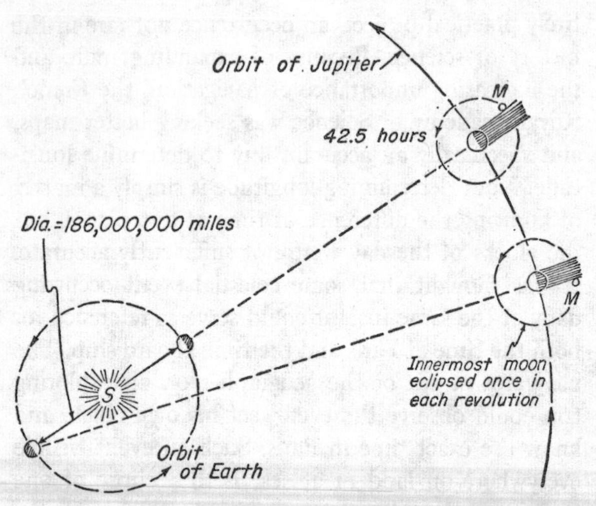

Fig. 1. ROEMER'S DEDUCTION. *Roemer had good reason to believe that Jupiter's innermost moon* (M) *took 42½ hours to complete its orbit around Jupiter. Therefore, the moon should enter eclipse behind Jupiter (or leave eclipse) every 42½ hours and follow a timetable constructed on 42½-hour intervals. But for most of the year actual observations of the eclipse lagged further and further behind the predicted timetable. The greatest lag, observed when the earth was in the position farthest from Jupiter, was 1320 seconds behind the observation at the nearest position. Roemer concluded that light was not instantaneous but traveled at finite velocity; therefore light must take longer and longer to reach the earth from Jupiter as the earth's orbit around the sun carries the earth farther and farther from Jupiter. The maximum lag of 1320 seconds, Roemer concluded, was the time it took light to travel across the earth's orbit. Though the contemporary figure*

who had been making very careful observations and computations of the eclipses, got a hunch.

Roemer's explanation was that the 1320 seconds (or 22 minutes) was the time light took to travel the distance between the earth's position closest to Jupiter and its position farthest from Jupiter, the two positions being six months apart. In other words, this extra distance traveled by light reflected from Jupiter's moon was the diameter of the earth's orbit around the sun (Fig. 1). This diameter in Roemer's day was thought to be approximately 182,000,000 miles, which, divided by 1320 seconds, gave him the figure 138,000 miles a second for the velocity of light.

At first glance Roemer's figure, with its error of almost 50,000 miles per second, may seem pretty preposterous, but think what he did accomplish. For the first time in the history of man a supposedly infinite motion was brought within the compass of reason and human measurement. Still more impressive, on his first try Roemer derived a figure whose *order of magnitude* is correct! And when you consider that refinements even today are being made in the measurement of the earth's orbital diameter and in the determination of the exact times of eclipse of Jupiter's moons, you will not wonder at his error. Today we know that the eclipse time lag is not Roemer's 22 minutes but about 16 minutes and 36 seconds, and our approximate figure for the orbital diameter is

---

for the orbital diameter was not very accurate and the eclipse observations were crude, Roemer's deduction gave a calculated velocity of light that was of the same order of magnitude as the best measurements we have today.

186,000,000 miles, not 182,000,000. With these modern figures, the calculation yields 186,000 miles per second for the velocity of light, and this is close to the best today's scientists have been able to manage.

One requirement of a good hypothesis is that it should be useful in making predictions that turn out to be correct. On the basis of his calculated speed of light, Roemer succeeded in forecasting the times of certain eclipses months in advance. In September 1676, for example, he predicted that in the following November a moon of Jupiter would reappear about ten minutes late. The tiny satellite co-operated, and Roemer's prediction came true to the second. In spite of this confirmation, however, Roemer's theory did not budge the Paris philosophers. But Isaac Newton and the great Dutch astronomer and physicist Christiaan Huygens did support the Dane. And eventually, in January 1729, the English astronomer James Bradley, using a somewhat different method of reasoning, independently confirmed Roemer's position. There no longer was any question. For scientists, Roemer had shattered the belief that light took no time at all, regardless of distance, to travel from source to observer.

Roemer had proved that the velocity of light, while tremendously great, was, indeed, finite and measurable. But his achievement, impressive as it was, still did not satisfy some scientists. His method of measurement depended on astronomical observations and required a long time to complete. What they wanted was a purely terrestrial method—one that they could perform in an earthly laboratory without resorting to points of reference outside the planet, one that they could keep completely under their own control. Had not the French physicist Father Marin Mersenne, a fellow student of Descartes, determined the speed of sound thirty-five years ago? Why could not the same be done with light?

THE FIRST TERRESTRIAL MEASUREMENT

The world of science had to wait almost two centuries for a solution of the problem. In 1849 Armand Hippolyte Fizeau, a French physicist wealthy enough to devote his time to research, devised a relatively simple experiment. Figure 2 shows his setup in a simplified form. He sent a beam of light from the source to a mirror *B*, which reflected the light to another mirror A. One station was at the home of Fizeau's father in Suresnes, the other in Montmartre in Paris, about 5.39 miles away. Between A and *B* was a toothed wheel, which he could rotate at regulated speeds. (You will recognize the stroboscope principle.) The teeth of the rotating wheel interrupted the light beam and chopped it into pulses. What was sent out was a succession of short flashes.

When the wheel was at rest in the proper position, the observer could see the image of the light source through the opening between two adjacent teeth. When the wheel was set in motion and the speed increased, there came a point at which the light pulse passing through one opening returned from A just in time for a tooth of the wheel to eclipse it. The observer saw nothing. When the wheel speed was increased further, the light reappeared and became

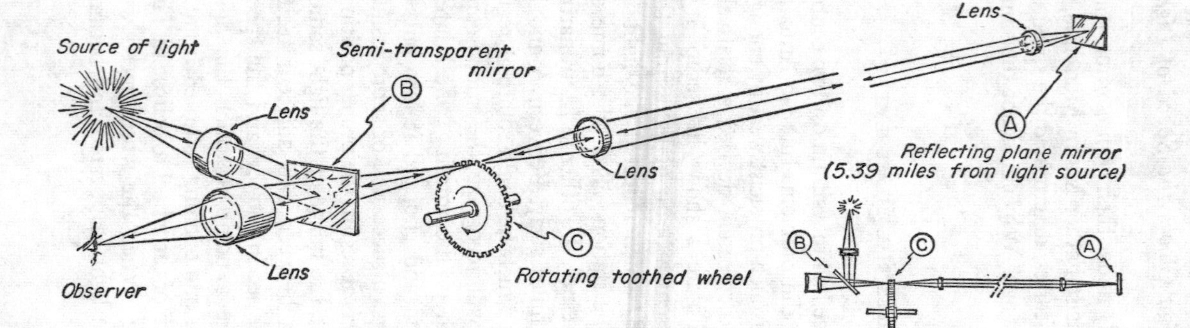

Fig. 2. FIZEAU'S APPARATUS. *One hundred and seventy-four years after Roemer's deduction, Fizeau used this apparatus to measure light speed under controlled conditions. The toothed wheel at C chopped the light beam into bursts. Fizeau measured the time it took a burst to travel from C to the mirror at A and back, a total distance of 10.78 miles. The weak point of the method was that the observer had to decide when the reflected light reached its brightest intensity. Such subjective judgments are poor criteria of physical experiment.*

brighter and brighter until it reached a maximum intensity. With a wheel which had 720 teeth on its circumference, Fizeau could detect this maximum intensity when the wheel was rotating at a speed of 25 revolutions a second. He then calculated the speed of light in this way:

The time required for the light to travel between stations and back would be the time needed for the wheel to rotate from one opening between teeth to the next opening, or $1/25 \times 1/720$, which equals 1/18,000 second. The distance traveled was twice the path between stations, or 10.78 miles. Hence, the speed of light was $10.78 \times 18{,}000$, or about 194,000 miles per second.

FOUCAULT'S IMPROVEMENT

When Fizeau announced his finding, the scientific world wondered whether this colossal speed, which would bring light to us from the sun in eight minutes and carry it around the earth in an eighth of a second, was a truly reliable figure. It seemed incredible that man with his crude and puny instruments could measure so tremendous a velocity. Light could travel the more than five miles between Fizeau's stations in 1/36,000 of a second? Impossible, many said. Yet Fizeau's figure did agree roughly with the speed Roemer had obtained. That could hardly be a coincidence.

Thirteen years later, while skeptics still doubted and made uncharitable remarks, Jean Foucault, a onetime medical student and the son of a Paris pub-

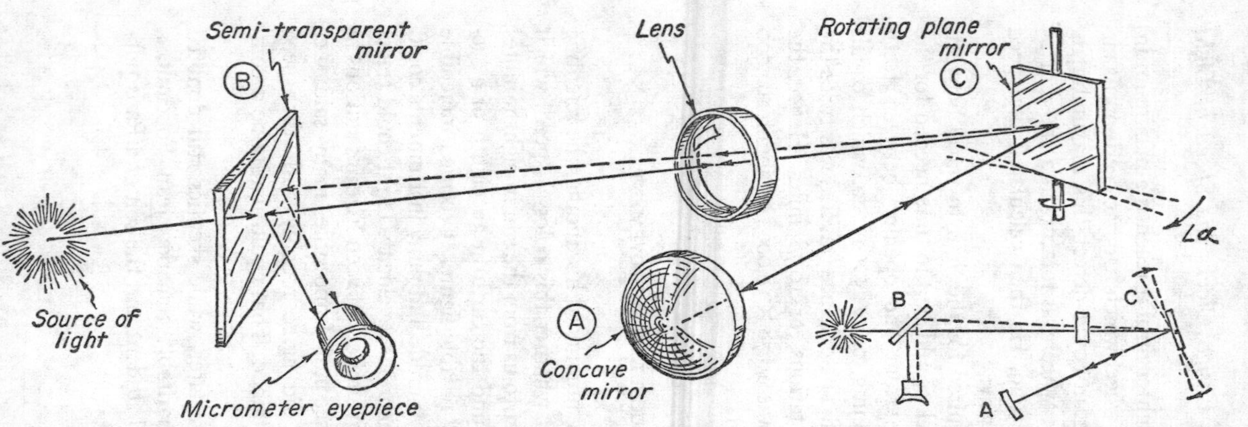

Fig. 3. FOUCAULT'S APPARATUS. *In this device, which Michelson refined for his measurements of light speed, the rotating plane mirror took the place of Fizeau's toothed wheel (Fig. 2). When the mirror was standing still or turning very slowly, the light was reflected to the semi-transparent mirror (B) along the solid line. When it was turning rapidly, the reflected light was displaced along the dotted line. The observer looking through the micrometer eyepiece could measure the amount of displacement on the semi-transparent mirror. This measurement gave him twice the angle α, which was the rotation of the mirror while light was traveling from C to the concave mirror (A) and back to C. Knowing the rotational speed of C, the distance from C to A and back, and the amount of rotation of C in the interval, the experimenter could readily calculate the speed of light.*

lisher, tried another method. He had worked with Fizeau for a few years and had given much thought to improving Fizeau's technique. Instead of using the notched wheel of Fizeau's experiment, he substituted a rotating mirror.

Foucault was greatly respected as a scientific investigator. In 1855 he won the coveted Copley Medal of the Royal Society of England for an ingenious and simple pendulum method of demonstrating the daily rotation of the earth on its axis. He also had invented a practical gyroscope. His introduction of the rotating mirror in the Fizeau experiment (proposed in 1842 by Dominique Arago but not tried) made it possible to shorten the path of the light beam from more than five miles to only 65.6 feet. The rotating mirror (Fig. 3) turned the returning light beam at a slight angle, which permitted measurements leading to calculation of the velocity. Foucault's figure for the speed of light in air was around 185,000 miles per second, about 9000 miles under Fizeau's. (Foucault also introduced a tube of water between the reflecting mirror and the rotating mirror to measure the speed of light in water. He found it to be less than in air.)

Ten years later Marie Alfred Cornu, professor of experimental physics at the Ecole Polytechnique, in Paris, went back to the toothed wheel but used one with 200 teeth. He obtained still another figure, 186,600 miles per second. There the matter stood when, in 1872, young Michelson was a senior at the United States Naval Academy, at Annapolis, Maryland, having passed an examination in optics in which the second question was, "Describe Foucault's apparatus for determining the velocity of light." None could have known it then, but Michelson's name was to loom larger than Fizeau's or Foucault's on the examination papers for the physics students of many generations to come.

CHAPTER II

Growing Up

The story of Albert Abraham Michelson is a chapter of that American saga of the nineteenth century that has had few counterparts in history. He was born on December 19, 1852, in the little town of Strelno, which was Polish in its population and tradition but at the time was in German territory. Near the Polish-German border, it was some eighty miles from Thorn, where Copernicus was born almost four centuries earlier. The Germans had occupied Strelno, and its province of Poznan, since Frederick the Great had helped to carve up Poland in 1772; it did not return to Poland until the close of World War I. Although he never showed much interest in his relatives who had stayed behind in the Old World, Michelson always took pleasure, or consolation, in regarding himself as a Pole—and for an ironic reason. "A Pole," he once remarked to his children, "is never happy."

Like thousands of others, the Michelsons came to the United States on the wave of immigration created in the European political upheavals of 1848. The liberal, democratic revolutions that had seemed to promise a new life for the Old World had crumbled and their collapse shook Europe. Widespread persecution followed, and many fled. America placed no obstacle in the way of these refugees; on the contrary, their talents were eagerly sought. The roster of those who came for haven and stayed to help build the United States is a long one. Abraham I. Jacobi, who spent two years behind bars before he escaped to America, became a great physician. Henry Flad, the engineer-inventor; Charles Mohr, the botanist; Leo Lesquereux, who became the leading paleobotanist of his day; Arnold Guyot, the celebrated Princeton University geologist—they were only a few of the scientists and intellectuals who sought refuge in the United States. Among the "forty-eighters" was Adolph Brandeis, whose son, Louis Dembitz Brandeis, was to be an outstanding justice of the Supreme Court of the United States. Franz Sigel, a general in the Union Army in the Civil War, and Carl Schurz, United States senator from Missouri, abandoned Europe to try their luck in America. It was an exodus of considerable magnitude in the same pattern as the flight of Jews and anti-Nazi intellectuals from Hitler's Germany.

FROM POLAND TO VIRGINIA CITY

Albert was two years old when the Michelsons made the trip. The father, Samuel, had owned a small dry-goods store. At the age of forty he had married pretty eighteen-year-old Rosalie Przlubska, daughter of a Polish physician. When persecution flared up with renewed ferocity, the Michelsons took their small savings and left for America. Mr. Michelson worked for a time as a jeweler in New York City but was not happy. He decided to join his sister, who had gone to California in the early Gold Rush days.

Gold had been discovered in 1848, when James W. Marshall picked up the first nugget in the village of Coloma. The discovery brought on a wild mining boom; in two years California became a state. The picture of an easier life in a successful business in the thriving new state appealed to Samuel Michelson. Rosalie was taken with the thought of a better life in a more healthful climate. They heard tales of merchants who grew prosperous overnight supplying dry goods to the mushrooming new towns and equipping pack trains. Samuel bought a store of dry goods in New York to be shipped around Cape Horn to San Francisco.

Then, how to get the family to California? There was no transcontinental railroad. The idea of making the overland trek in a covered wagon was not engaging—they had read of hundreds who had suffered and died along the way. By ship around Cape Horn took too long, from three to six months. Although a comparatively easy journey, it was tedious and expensive. On the advice of Samuel's sister, they chose the quickest, if not the safest, route. From New York they went by ship to the Isthmus of Panama. There they disembarked and traveled across the neck of land by muleback, in native boats and carts, menaced by scurvy, cholera, Chagres fever, and bandits. At the end of this second leg of the journey, they fought for passage on one of the creaking old vessels that plied the Pacific coast. They stayed only a brief time in

San Francisco, then headed for the gold diggings. In the summer of 1856 the elder Michelson opened a small dry-goods store at Murphy's Camp, or just plain Murphy's, in Calaveras County. (In 1865 Mark Twain immortalized the county in his story "The Celebrated Jumping Frog of Calaveras County." Murphy's was not far from the scene of the story.)

As any small boy would, young Albert had a great time among the boisterous miners and picturesque peddlers of this frontier settlement. He must have met many characters like those Bret Harte described in "The Luck of Roaring Camp" and "The Outcasts of Poker Flat." "Snowshoe" Thompson, the all but indestructible mailman who carried letters and packages across the Sierras in the dead of winter for twenty years, often visited Murphy's; Albert must have known him by sight at least. One of the local prospectors had a lifelong influence on the youngster. This man was a fine musician. On visits to the store he became fond of young Albert. He introduced him to the violin and taught him to play. The lessons struck a responsive chord. Albert practiced diligently in his spare time and acquired an art that gave him pleasure and sustained him throughout his life.

When Albert was thirteen, his family sent him to San Francisco to attend the Boys High School. He lived at the home of the school principal, Theodore Bradley, who recognized the boy's exceptional mechanical abilities and encouraged him. He placed Albert in charge of the school's simple scientific equipment and paid him three dollars a month to keep it in repair. But Albert developed few friendships at school and was lonely. (He also was frightened one night when his bed suddenly slid across the room—an earthquake.) It was with no reluctance then, in the summer of 1869, his high school education complete, that he left San Francisco for home.

By then home no longer was at Murphy's but in the rear of a store at 24 South C Street in Virginia City, in Storey County, Nevada. California had failed to fulfill her golden promise to the Michelsons. The mining around Murphy's had petered out, and discovery of silver, in 1859, in the fabulous Comstock Lode brought prospectors rushing to Nevada. In one year Virginia City, built over the Lode, became the most famous camp in the West. It was there that Mark Twain became a newspaper reporter in 1862 and started one of America's great literary careers. Within a few years Virginia City could boast of its own millionaires and of not a few mansions. By 1875 Storey County had a population of 35,000. There were Irish and Cornish miners, a sizable representation of Chinese, altogether some 10,000 of foreign birth. There were those who worked and those who speculated and others who preyed on both.

TRYING FOR COLLEGE

Such was the colorful, bustling, rowdy environment of Albert's youth. He found the miners fascinating and made a hobby of collecting the many-colored ores they dug out of the ground, but mining as a profession had no appeal for him. Friends who gathered at the store often talked about Albert's future—he had shown an unusual aptitude for mathematics. His mother wanted to see him in the medical profession, but his father was a realist. College would mean board and lodging in some distant city, books, and tuition; it would be a real hardship for the whole family. True, Congress seven years before had passed the Morrill Land Grant Act, and agricultural and industrial colleges were being established in each state, either independently or in connection with state universities. Massachusetts Institute of Technology, Worcester Polytechnic Institute, and the Columbia School of Mines were among these land-grant colleges. But they were all in the East, far away, and too expensive. The Michelsons had only a small business, no other property, no money.

There were quite a few mouths for Samuel to feed. Rosalie had given birth to nine children, of whom six survived. A baby brother had just joined the brood, sixteen years after the birth of Albert. Miriam, last of the Michelson children, was born the following year. As a family, they left their mark. Pauline became a schoolteacher. Miriam was a newspaper writer and drama critic, author of several novels, including *In the Bishop's Carriage* (1904). Charles grew up to be a brilliant newspaperman and, as its shrewd director of publicity, one of the influential figures of the Democratic New Deal of the 1930s.

One possible solution of Albert's future presented itself. Why not the United States Naval Academy? It offered an excellent education, an honorable career, a chance to serve his adopted land, prestige for the family. Furthermore, accepted candidates received traveling expenses to the Academy at Annapolis and, while cadets, pay of $500 a year and "one ration." The Naval Academy had been established twenty-four years before, in part by the efforts of a distinguished scientist, the oceanographer Lieutenant Matthew Fontaine Maury, U.S.N.

The idea of trying for admission pleased Albert. Appointment to the Academy had been submitted to competition by public advertisement—open to all Nevada boys between the ages of fourteen and eighteen. Albert and nine others took the written examination for cadet midshipman on June 10, 1869, in the Virginia City courthouse. Albert passed creditably in reading, writing, spelling, arithmetic, geography, and English grammar but did not get the appointment. In spite of more than a hundred letters and telegrams in behalf of Albert, the appointment went to fifteen-year-old James W. Blakely of Treasure City, who had tied with Albert in the examination. Blakely was the son of a poor Civil War veteran who had lost his right arm.

Albert was not easily discouraged. He decided to appeal through his congressman, Thomas Fitch, to the President of the United States for any other vacancy that might exist at Annapolis. The chances were not rosy, but Albert thought it worth the effort.

AN INTERVIEW WITH PRESIDENT GRANT

Washington, D.C., was a long way from Virginia City. The last spike in the first transcontinental railroad had been driven only a few weeks earlier, at Promontory Point, Utah, on May 10, 1869, and train connections were poor. But Albert started off, and he had to travel by carriage, horseback, on foot, and by rail before he finally arrived at the capital. He had armed himself with a letter from the father of the successful candidate as well as recommendations from his high school principal and his congressman, who described Albert as "zealous, loyal, studious, and uncommonly bright." The principal's letter said Albert "had been graduated with honors and exhibited great aptitude for scientific pursuits."

It was common knowledge that at a certain hour every day President Grant took his dog for an airing on the White House grounds. Young Albert waited for him on the White House steps. The President listened to the sixteen-year-old's request and explained that all the ten special appointments-at-large had been made. But he did take the time to hear Albert's plea and to read all the letters. "I'll make you proud of me if I get the appointment," Albert assured him.

President Grant remembered an odd sort of letter he had received recently from Fitch, in which the congressman had cited a reason for appointing Albert that was nothing if not practical. "Had I felt at liberty to be governed by considerations of political expediency," the congressman had written, "I should have selected him. His father is a prominent and influential merchant of Virginia City, and a member of the Israelite persuasion, who by his example and influence has largely contributed to the success of our cause, and induced many of his co-religionists to do the same. These people are a powerful element in our politics, the boy who is uncommonly bright and studious is a pet among them, and I do most steadfastly believe that his appointment at *your* hand would do more to fasten these people to the Republican cause, than anything else that could be done. The Union people of Nevada . . . will demonstrate to you hereafter, that the 'strong-box' of the nation will be the strong-hold of your administration on this coast. I know you can greatly please them and strengthen us by making this appointment, and I take the liberty of expressing my deep solicitude that it be made."

This kind of argument struck home. After pondering a bit, President Grant turned young Michelson over to a naval aide, who sent the youth to Annapolis to see Vice-Admiral David D. Porter, Superintendent of the Naval Academy. One of the ten presidential appointees might fail the examination and leave an opening. Albert waited three days in Annapolis and was about to go back to Washington for a final plea to Grant when a messenger arrived with news that an additional opening had been created. Albert was to receive the "eleventh appointment." Many years later Michelson pointed out that his career as a scientist stemmed from "an illegal act."

And so, on June 28, 1869, at the request of the Secretary of the Navy, Albert Abraham Michelson presented himself to the Medical Board, which found him "free from deformity and disease and imperfections of the senses." On the day following, the Academic Board examined him in reading, writing, spelling, arithmetic, and English grammar and found him duly qualified. Three days later he filed an affidavit of his loyalty and his willingness to serve in the United States Navy for eight years. Aged sixteen and a half years, he was admitted officially to the Naval Academy as cadet midshipman.

MIDSHIPMAN MICHELSON

The four years at Annapolis passed quickly and, except for a brush with a fellow midshipman in the senior year, without extracurricular incident. This episode has been related by Bradley A. Fiske, later rear admiral. One day Michelson was in charge of a small detachment and rebuked Fiske for being lazy in execution of an order. "Dress back, Mr. Fiske," he ordered. Fiske resented Michelson's tone and challenged "Mike the fiddler" to a fight after dinner. It was the traditional way of settling differences, and Michelson accepted the challenge.

The fight lasted exactly one minute. The referee, observing that Fiske could see with neither eye, stepped in. For the next eight days Fiske was on sick leave, long enough to realize that it was a mistake to tangle with the Academy's best lightweight boxer. Michelson, who had taken lessons in fencing and boxing, was always proud of his health and physical prowess. He played good tennis and tried to keep fit almost to the year of his death. Once when he was in his seventies he went to a friend's home for dinner. To the usual perfunctory question about the state of his health, he replied, with what struck his host as unnecessary emphasis, "I never felt better in my life, and I played two sets of tennis this afternoon."

Michelson and twenty-eight others received their Academy diplomas on May 31, 1873, all that were left of a starting class of eighty-six. Except in science and mathematics, his scholastic record was nothing remarkable. He ranked ninth in over-all standing and ninth, too, in number of demerits. He had been charged with 129 infractions and on several occasions had done time in the brig. Nevertheless, he ranked first in optics and acoustics and second in mathematics, dynamics, heat, and climatology. In chemistry and statics he stood third and was near the top of the class in technical grammar. He had done well enough in mechanics, electricity, and physical geography. He was really not interested in warfare, gunnery, or seamanship, and upon graduation he ranked twenty-fifth in seamanship. He was near the bottom of the class in history and composition. It was characteristic of Michelson that when he was not interested in a subject, he neglected it.

At that time the Superintendent of the Academy was John L. Worden. He had been commanding officer of the *Monitor*, the ironclad that saved the Union fleet from the Confederate ironclad *Merrimac* eleven years earlier in Chesapeake Bay. (John Ericsson, a Swedish engineer who became an American citizen, designed the *Monitor*.) Worden's background did not incline him toward sympathy for Michelson's preferential academic shortcomings. He is said to have told the midshipman, "If you'd give less attention to those scientific things and more to your naval gunnery, there might come a time when you would know enough to be of some use to your country."

James Whistler, one of America's most famous painters, was dismissed from the United States Military Academy, at West Point, after he had failed a chemistry examination. Years later Whistler observed that if he had known that the element silicon was normally not a gas, he might have turned out to be a major general instead of a painter. Who knows what might have happened to Michelson if he had been first in seamanship? Worden was right in one respect: Michelson was not destined to distinguish himself as an officer of the line. But Worden was terribly in error about Michelson's eventual service to his country.

AN INSTRUCTOR AT ANNAPOLIS

Soon after graduation Michelson was ordered to duty aboard the U.S.S. *Monongahela*. He served the customary two years at sea on her and three other ships. In the summer of 1874 he was promoted to ensign, and at the end of his stint at sea was offered the post of instructor of physics and chemistry at the Academy. He gladly accepted. To Michelson the teaching job offered security and an opportunity to continue his studies. He knew the assignment would be easy; he would have plenty of leisure. "Any officer in the Navy could have filled it," he wrote. "The classroom method of recitation then in vogue made it easy. All I had to do was to keep a few textbook pages ahead of the cadets."

Physics had attracted Michelson more than chemistry. He became more and more interested in optics, and he began to study it in earnest. But life at the Academy was not all study, even for him. He played tennis regularly and began to paint as a hobby—he had been first in his class in drawing. And often he relaxed with his violin. There was even time for the girls, or, at least, for one girl.

Commander (later Rear Admiral) William T. Sampson, who was to command the American naval forces that smashed the Spanish squadron off Santiago de Cuba in 1898, headed the Department of Natural and Experimental Philosophy (what we now would call physics) at the Academy. His wife had a niece, Margaret McLean Heminway, who occasionally visited them. One evening the Sampsons invited Michelson to meet her. Actually, they had met before, in England, when Michelson's ship was in port there. Michelson was making the usual tour of Westminster Abbey and had stopped at the garlanded tomb of Charles Dickens. Near by stood a young girl, traveling with her parents from New Rochelle, New York, and they had passed the time of day. She was Miss Heminway.

Margaret, eighteen, was beautiful. Albert made a striking figure. About five feet eight inches tall, he had a trim physique. His forehead was broad, his features finely chiseled. Jet-black hair topped his handsome head. It was his flashing, deep-set hazel eyes that first attracted the girl to the quiet, rather shy cadet. After the dinner at the Sampsons', they began seeing each other regularly; soon they were engaged. In the spring of 1877 Margaret and Albert were married at the Heminway home in New Rochelle. Their first child, named Albert Heminway, was born at the Academy in January 1878. The second child, Truman, was born the next year. Eventually Albert Heminway Michelson entered the United States consular service. Truman became a distinguished ethnologist at the Smithsonian Institution, an authority on the Fox Indians.

Up to this point, where we find him settled into family life and reasonably secure in his position as an Academy instructor, the story of Albert Michelson, while by no means a commonplace one, was not so extraordinary that it plotted an inevitable course for his future. But, as we shall see, it was an auspicious time for physicists interested in optics, and especially for one as determined and dedicated as Michelson.

CHAPTER III

The First Measurements

In the winter of 1876 the eminent English physicist John Tyndall came to America to lecture on light and in the course of his travels had the opportunity to survey the state of science in the United States.

"I have been unable to see anything in the constitution of your society," he said, "to prevent a student from bestowing the most steadfast devotion on pure science. If great scientific results are not achieved in America, it is not to the small agitations of society that I should be disposed to ascribe the defect, but to the fact that the men among you who possess the endowments necessary for a profound scientific inquiry are laden with duties of administration, of tuition so heavy as to be utterly incompatible with the continuous and tranquil meditation which original investigation demands."

To these observations, far from unfamiliar in our own day, Tyndall added a word of advice: "You have scientific genius amongst you. Take all unnecessary impediments out of its way. Keep your scientific eye upon the originator of knowledge. Give him the freedom necessary for his researches, not demanding from him so-called practical results—above all things avoiding the question which ignorance so often addresses to genius, 'What is the use of your work?'" Tyndall's advice is as sound today, and almost in as great need of constant repetition, as it was nearly a century ago.

Tyndall had not chosen light casually as the topic for his American lectures. The subject was becoming increasingly important to the world of science. Only three years before, in 1873, James Clerk Maxwell, one of the truly great men of physics, had published his monumental treatise, *Electricity and Magnetism,* which in the language of mathematical equations linked light to electricity and magnetism, postulated the existence of electromagnetic (radio) waves, and attributed to them and to light waves the same velocity. "We can scarcely avoid the inference," Maxwell had written, "that light consists in the transverse undulations of the same medium which is the cause of electric and magnetic phenomena." Maxwell's work excited physicists all over the world. The speed of light was recognized as one of the most important and fundamental numbers of nature. It was crucial to the solution of some of the most compelling problems of all physical science.

A NEW PRECISION

To find the speed of light with the ultimate precision was a challenge that already had sparked Michelson's ambition. "The fact that the velocity of light is so far beyond the conception of the human intellect, coupled with the extraordinary accuracy with which it may be measured, makes this determination one of the most fascinating problems that fall to the lot of the investigator," he wrote.

Michelson was not satisfied with the measurements that had been made. They involved too many errors. Perhaps he could do better. In November 1877, several months after his marriage, he hit upon a minor modification of Foucault's method that he thought would be vital. Dispensing with the Frenchman's concave mirror, Michelson substituted a plane mirror and lens (Fig. 4) and shifted the rotating mir-

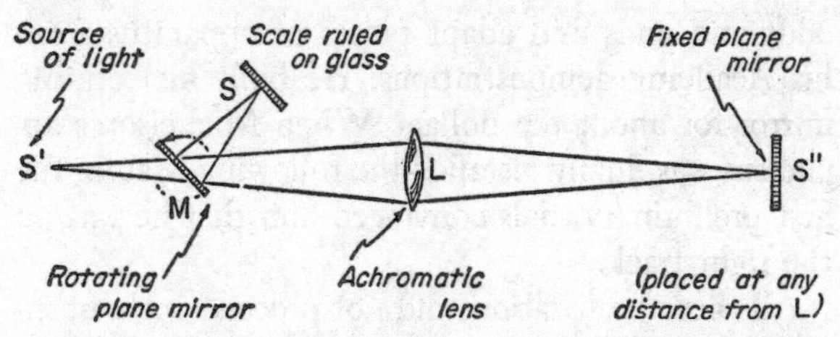

Fig. 4. FIRST MICHELSON APPARATUS. *In 1878 Michelson made his first measurement of the speed of light with an apparatus essentially the same as Foucault's* (*Fig.* 3) *but incorporating minor improvements. The lens arrangement allowed the light path to be of any length. The ruled scale on the glass plate* (S) *made it easier to read accurately the displacement of the reflected beam from the rotating mirror.*

ror from its original position. With this arrangement the light path in the experiment could be almost any length without loss of intensity of the beam. Michelson planned to use two plane mirrors 500 feet apart in his experiment, one fixed and one rotating. The rotating mirror would be mounted on a brick pier in front of the light source and would make 130 revolutions per second, driven by air blasts from a bellows. The vibrations of two tuning forks would check the rotational speed of the mirror.

Michelson had no money for expensive apparatus. In those days pure research was not subsidized by industrial concerns or rich private foundations, and the support from government funds was limited indeed. College professors accomplished what they could in their dingy laboratories in the few hours left to them between classes. Michelson had to gather odds and ends and adapt pieces of apparatus from his Academy demonstrations. He built his rotating mirror for about ten dollars. When Michelson's apparatus was finally installed the following March, the first preliminary trials convinced him that he was on the right track.

All these preparations did not proceed without interruption. His first child was born in January, an event distracting to young fathers, and there was a mishap in the laboratory. One of the mirrors was thrown out of its bearings on a trial run and smashed; other problems came up. Michelson looked around for help. He wrote to Simon Newcomb, the astronomer, who a decade earlier had suggested that Foucault's experiment should be repeated. Michelson's first request to Newcomb was simple enough—he asked for a piece of glass to replace the broken mirror. Then, having read a *Tribune* extract of a paper by Newcomb, he wrote another letter, which said, in part:

"Hearing through Captain Sampson that you were interested in my own experiments, I trust I am not taking too great a liberty in laying before you a brief account of what I have done. . . . It would give me great pleasure, sir, if you would honor me with an interview, in which you would advise me how to arrange some of the details so as to insure good results.

Believe me, Sir
Your obedient Servant
ALBERT MICHELSON
Ensign, USN"

In May, without waiting to complete the project, Michelson submitted his first communication to the *American Journal of Science* (1),* in the form of a letter to the editor. It was entitled "On a Method of Measuring the Velocity of Light." It consisted of but nineteen lines of type and a single diagram and gave no data. The method to be used was all that Michelson described.

After a series of ten experiments "made under difficulties," Michelson went to a St. Louis meeting of the American Association for the Advancement of Science and laid before its members a new determination of the speed of light in air—186,508 miles per second. His paper, "Experimental Determination of the Velocity of Light," appeared in the April 1879 issue of the *American Journal of Science* (2, 3) and thence found its way to the Virginia City newspaper. It was not just the piece of news the Nevada miners had been holding their breaths to hear, but to the world of science it was historic.

* This and succeeding numbers refer to the list of Michelson's papers in Appendix I.

NEWCOMB'S SUPPORT

In the St. Louis audience was Newcomb, who, as retiring president of the Association, had delivered an address on the simplicity and universality of the laws of nature. Young Michelson's boldness and the skill implied in his experiment thrilled Newcomb, along with the other scientists, and rekindled his interest in the velocity of light. Almost immediately he sought the opinion of the National Academy of Sciences on the propriety of asking the government for money to carry the experiments further. An Academy committee agreed that the money should be made available, and a year later the Secretary of the Navy recommended a congressional appropriation of $5000. Newcomb, who was a commissioned officer in the now extinct Navy Corps of Professors, was put in charge, his duties to be carried out at the Naval Observatory and the Nautical Almanac Office, both in Washington, D.C.

Though it does not sound like much nowadays, the $5000 was a relatively large sum of money then, enough for Newcomb to plan a new set of experiments toward finding a still more precise value of the speed of light. He went to nearby Annapolis to talk the project over with Michelson and found the young instructor at work on the problem. A year or so earlier "a private gentleman" (who turned out to be Michelson's father-in-law) had put up $2000 to help the young experimenter to improve his technique with better apparatus. Michelson ordered a new mirror from the telescope builder Alvan Clark and started looking around for an air-driven turbine wheel to rotate the mirror.

Michelson had been making observations along the north sea wall of the Academy in a frame structure forty-five feet long and seven feet above the ground built to house the rotating mirror, engine, arc lamp, and other equipment. About 2000 feet away Michelson had had built another brick structure to enclose the brick pier for the other mirror. There was no road or walk between the two buildings, and when the ground was covered with snow or soggy with mud, it was time-wasting and troublesome to trudge back and forth. But Michelson took the difficulties in stride. He had received help from Professor A. M. Mayer of the Stevens Institute of Technology, Hoboken, New Jersey, in checking the mirror rotation, and two Academy men were making independent readings to avoid bias of the observer.

Newcomb's visit flattered Michelson; he would be happy to take part in the new project. That fall he was transferred from the Naval Academy to the Nautical Almanac Office. Newcomb set up an experiment station at Fort Myer, Virginia, on a hill overlooking the Potomac River. The distant reflecting mirror was a mile and a half away, on the grounds of the old Naval Observatory. Later the reflector was moved to the base of the Washington Monument. Observations were made there in the summers of 1881 and 1882.

But Michelson did not stay long with Newcomb. At the age of twenty-seven he felt an urgent need of further training in optics and of fresh inspiration, and his eyes turned toward the science centers of the Old World. Not until 1882 did he return to his relentless pursuit of the precise velocity of light. In that year, in a new job at the Case School of Applied Science, at Cleveland, Ohio, he took up where he had left off. He repeated the velocity experiment another twenty times and announced a new value for the velocity of light—299,853 kilometers (a little more than 186,000 miles) per second. It remained the accepted figure for forty-five years, and when it finally gave way to a more precise figure, Michelson again was the man who found it. In this experiment he had no rival.

There is an anecdote of his first year at Case that illustrates Michelson the scientist better than any other. One day when the optical path for his experiment was being surveyed on the north side of the tracks of the New York, Chicago & St. Louis Railroad, some reporters approached to ask what was going on. Michelson replied that he was measuring the speed of light. "What are you doing that for?" was the next question. "Because it is such fun," Michelson said. Fifty years later when the great Albert Einstein asked him a similar question, Michelson gave him the same answer.

CHAPTER IV

The Elusive Ether

After Michelson left the Newcomb project, he received a leave of absence from the Navy and sailed for Europe in 1880 with his wife and children. It was a well-charted course for American scientists. Except for the newly founded Johns Hopkins University, there was no institution in the United States wholly devoted to graduate work, and especially to scientific research. Josiah Willard Gibbs, destined to become America's greatest theoretical physicist and Yale University's least understood and appreciated professor; Asa Gray, the botanist; James Dana, the geologist; Othniel Marsh and Edward Cope, the paleontologists; Ira Remsen and Eben N. Horsford, the chemists; and William H. Welch, the medical man, all had made the same pilgrimage. If a scientist wanted to learn at firsthand the latest developments in his field, Europe was the place for him.

For nearly two years Michelson roamed the universities of Germany and France. He absorbed all the knowledge he could from the great men of European physics. He attended the lectures of Hermann von Helmholtz, the world-famous professor of theoretical physics at the University of Berlin, and did some laboratory work there. He attacked mechanics, in which he had only an elementary course at the Academy, and the calculus. He worked at the University of Heidelberg, the College of France, and the Ecole Polytechnique, in Paris. At the last he met Marie Cornu and Eleuthère Mascart, who later wrote a book on optics, and had a chance to discuss his own experiments with them.

In February 1881 Michelson wrote the Secretary of the Navy asking for a six months' extension of his leave and permission to stay abroad. It was granted. He had every intention of returning to the Academy and would have been satisfied with a Navy professorship. But it was not forthcoming. O. Wolcott Gibbs, chemist and professor of applied science at Harvard University, tried to help him in this ambition. Gibbs wrote a long letter to the Superintendent of the United States Coast Guard, physicist Julius E. Hilgard:

"Can't you do something to help Michelson to get one of the two professorships of Mathematics in the Navy? His letters of recommendation were sent in long ago and were very strong as he is a real brilliant fellow. If he does not get this place he will be lost to science. All that is necessary, I believe, is to get the President to say a word to the Secretary of the Navy who does not seem to be able to make up his mind. I consider it a *matter of real importance to this country to keep such a man and give him a chance to work. . . .*"

For a year nothing happened. Michelson made his own decision. On September 30, 1881, he resigned his commission in the Navy, having served twelve years and two months. The decision was eased by an offer from the Case School of Applied Science, which was just being established. The Case trustees offered him the first professorship of physics and money to continue his studies in Europe and to buy equipment for his future laboratory. They also granted him leave of absence for the year 1881–82 to continue his research.

HUYGENS AND NEWTON ON THE ETHER

These months in Europe, the meetings with the most famous physicists of the day, kept Michelson's mind in ferment. More and more, as he pondered the nature of light, he reverted to a fundamental question of increasing importance to physics. It was commonly supposed that light was propagated through the "luminiferous ether," which filled all space and was not solid, liquid, or gas but had some of their properties. Did this "luminiferous ether" actually exist? Could its existence be experimentally proved or disproved? This was a big idea, and big ideas attracted Michelson.

The ether concept went back to the earliest efforts to understand the phenomenon of light in properly scientific terms. Christiaan Huygens, the Dutch mathematician, astronomer, and physicist, was the first to fashion such a theory of light; he communicated his thoughts to the French Academy of Sciences in 1678. According to Huygens, luminous bodies, such as the incandescent sun or flaming torches, set up vibrations, or waves, that travel outward to the eye of the observer. Scientists had already established that vibrations of some material objects, a piece of metal or even the gases of the atmosphere, created sound. The vibrations set up by a clanging bell, for example, traveled outward in all directions just as ripples travel from a spot where a pebble has been dropped into water. If a bell were struck in a vacuum, with no air to transmit the undulations, there would be no sound. So it is with light, said Huygens. But that was not the whole story, and Huygens himself did not believe it to be as simple as all that. Light could travel through a vacuum, though presumably there was nothing material present to carry Huygens' hypothetical waves. Then what did carry them?

The "ether," a concept dating back to ancient times, was Huygens' answer. The ether was the medium that carried his light waves.

"Ether" is derived from a Greek word meaning air, sky, or the upper regions. Ancient philosophers used it in explaining the motions of planets and other celestial bodies; they spoke of many different ethers occupying different regions in space. Aristotle sanctioned its use and considered it a sort of fifth element. "The earth is surrounded by water," he wrote, "the water by air, the air by the ether. Beyond the ether there is nothing more."

Isaac Newton experimented and speculated about light for almost forty years before he published his comprehensive explanation of many optical phenomena. His book finally appeared in 1704 under the title *Opticks*, or *A Treatise on the Reflections, Refractions, Inflections and Colours of Light*. Unlike his famous *Principia*, which was written in Latin and intended for the specialist, this book was published in simple English the laymen might understand. It was fascinating to read and contained a wealth of experimental detail.

An atomist at heart, Newton, like some of the ancients, believed light to be composed of small particles, or "corpuscles," emitted by the source of the light. Each particle was too small to be seen or measured, but the theory could explain, nevertheless, many light phenomena—its propagation in straight lines, its reflection from surfaces, its refraction at the boundary of media of different densities, its absorption and its pressure. But Newton himself was not satisfied that his particle theory explained all the phenomena of light. It did not explain interference, which he called "inflections." This is the phenomenon that occurs when different wave motions meet; the vibration is strengthened, diminished, or canceled altogether. (We shall have much more to say later about interference.) Newton himself introduced "ether waves" and suggested that *both* the corpuscle and wave concepts were needed to explain the phenomena of light. His complete acceptance of the ether is implicit in these words he wrote about gravitation: "To suppose that one body may act upon another at a distance through a vacuum, without the mediation of anything else, is to me so great an absurdity that I believe no man, who has in philosophical matters a complete faculty for thinking, can ever fall into."

So, for many centuries, to deny the existence of the ether was as foolish as saying that the ocean did not need water for boats to float on. Whatever it was, the ether pervaded all space; it permeated all matter; it even was present between the atoms of solid matter. Agreement on the necessity of ether, however, did not preclude debate over its nature. Ether had the properties of a solid of great rigidity, said some. It was thin and tenuous, argued others. That at different times under different conditions, the ether, like cobbler's wax, had different characteristics, was a common analogy used by others, Michelson among them.

COULD THE ETHER BE MEASURED?

Indeed, the behavior of light did seem to demand some medium capable of carrying wavelike radiations through millions of miles without weakening or diluting the initial energy. But, Michelson wondered, was there really such a thing as the ether? Could science in the laboratory materialize or exorcise this theoretical ghost so conveniently invoked to explain scientific dilemmas? Was it only a gossamer of physics without body, shape, or form? Was it, as the British statesman Lord Salisbury suggested, only a noun for the verb "to undulate"?

And, furthermore, was this mysterious ether, if it did exist, stationary? Or did the earth in its daily rotation on its axis and its annual revolution around the sun drag the ether along with it as some, like the English physicist and mathematician Sir George G. Stokes, liked to believe? There were those who welcomed the fixed, or stationary, ether. Among the proponents of the stationary-ether concept was the brilliant Frenchman Augustin Fresnel (1788–1827), who co-ordinated all the experimental data on light phenomena into a mathematical theory of wave motion and proved that light waves are transverse. (In transverse wave motion the oscillations are at right angles to the direction of wave travel. Water-surface waves are transverse, as are the waves that run along a rope when you shake one end of it.) Many looked with favor on the notion of the stationary ether because it provided a needed frame of reference in space in order to measure *absolute motion* as opposed to relative motion. The term "absolute" designated a quality that all observers anywhere in the universe could accept as fact. Was the velocity of light an absolute? Was it, that is to say, the same for all observers regardless of the source of light or the observers' positions?

The question demanded an incontrovertible answer. It was cosmic in scope, profound in implications. The great Clerk Maxwell, in an article on the ether which he had contributed to the ninth edition of the Encyclopædia Britannica, had posed the problem.

"If it were possible," he wrote, "to determine the velocity of light by observing the time it takes to travel between one station and another on the earth's surface, we might by comparing the observed velocity in opposite directions determine the velocity of the ether with respect to these terrestrial stations."

In a letter published in 1879 in the British scientific journal *Nature* just before his death, at the age of forty-eight, Maxwell expressed his doubt of man's ability to find the answer. It is possible that Michelson read the letter; in any event, its unsolved problem lay ahead of him. To find the answer almost became an obsession.

It might have been presumptuous of the young American to think he could find the key older and much more experienced European scientists had missed, but what he had in mind was really a fairly simple experiment. He took his cue from an idea of Sir Oliver Lodge, an eminent British scientist. Lodge had said: "A deep-sea fish has probably no means of apprehending the existence of water; it is too uniformly immersed in it, and that is our condition in regard to the ether."

Michelson's reasoning went like this. Let us assume that the ether is something material that pervades and surrounds the earth. Let us suppose, further, that this ether is not in motion but stationary. Then it should be possible for an observer perched securely on the earth's surface to detect an "ether wind" as he rushes through space on the earth moving in its orbit around the sun. The observer should feel, or be able to detect, an ether wind just as the sailor on the deck of a moving ship feels the wind blowing across his face though the air is calm.

THE ETHER TEST

Michelson turned his plans and calculations over and over in his mind; it kept him awake at night. This ether sea in which we are immersed as fish are immersed in water should offer an obstacle to the passage of light. It should hold light back, and the slowing down should be measurable. You can see the problem clearly in this analogy. A swimmer knows, though he may not understand why, that it is easier to swim *across* a moving body of water and back than it is to swim the same distance downstream or upstream and then back to the starting point. Similarly, many a fisherman has learned that it takes longer to row a boat upstream and back to the starting point than to row across and back.

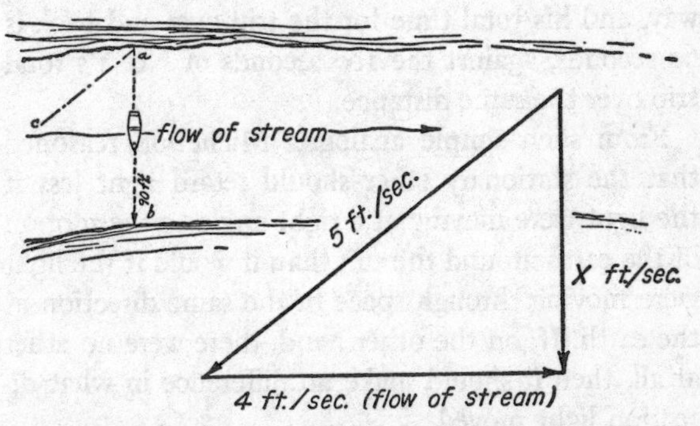

Fig. 5. THE ROWER ANALOGY. *It takes the rower 100 seconds to row 90 feet downstream and back but only 60 seconds to row 90 feet across the current and back.*

This fact can be illustrated (Fig. 5) with an easy calculation. Two men both can row at the rate of 5 feet per second in still water. The stream on which they are boating flows at the rate of 4 feet per second and is 90 feet wide. Rower No. 1 rows his boat 90 feet downstream and then back. Going downstream, he travels 9 feet per second; returning, he makes only 1 foot per second. His total time then is $90/9+90/1=100$ seconds. When Rower No. 2 crosses the stream, his rate of travel may be represented as one of the perpendicular sides of a right triangle whose other perpendicular side is the stream speed of 4 and whose hypotenuse is 5, the speed at which he can row in still water. The square of the hypotenuse equals the sum of the squares of the other two sides, or $5^2 = 4^2 + x^2$, and x, his actual rate of travel, equals 3. Therefore, he takes 90/3, or 30 seconds, to cross each way, and his total time for the trip over and back is 60 seconds, against the 100 seconds of No. 1's total trip over the same distance.

From such simple analogies Michelson reasoned that the stationary ether should retard light less if the light were moving at a right angle to the motion of the earth around the sun than it would if the light were moving through space in the same direction as the earth. If, on the other hand, there were no ether at all, then it should make no difference in what direction light moved.

The plan of his experiment, then, was this. He would send one beam of light through a measured distance in one direction and another beam of light an equal distance but at a right angle to the direction of the first. He would dispatch both beams at the same instant and have them reflected back to the same starting point. Now, if the ether were a reality, the two pencils of light, like our two oarsmen, would return to the starting point at slightly different times and demonstrate one characteristic of wave motion, an *interference effect*. That is, the waves of the two beams would cross each other and produce those alternate bands of light known as a fringe system.

Interference, as we have said, occurs when two waves meet, or *interfere*. Where the crest of one wave meets the trough of another, the wave motion cancels, and the medium at that point is in an undisturbed state. If the crest of one wave meets the crest of another, it strengthens, or *reinforces*, the wave motion. There are gradations between cancellation and total reinforcement.

You can see this phenomenon vividly if you study the waves in a ripple tank or any shallow tank of water. For a very crude demonstration, hold the tips of your forefingers several inches apart and dip them into the water simultaneously to start two circular waves. Keep dipping and try to keep the intervals of dipping as regular as you can. As the two series of circular waves meet, you can see the interference pattern. The areas of cancellation, where the water remains undisturbed, form *nodal lines* radiating out somewhat like wheel spokes. Between the nodal lines the wave motion continues.

In the same way, when the crest of one light wave meets the trough of another light wave, there is cancellation of light, and if you look through a small telescope or see the image on a screen, you will see alternate light and dark bands. The dark bands occur where there is cancellation. If, on the contrary, the waves arrive at the screen, or telescope, in the same phase—that is, crest on crest and trough on trough—no dark band appears (Fig. 6).

This phenomenon of interference was first demon-

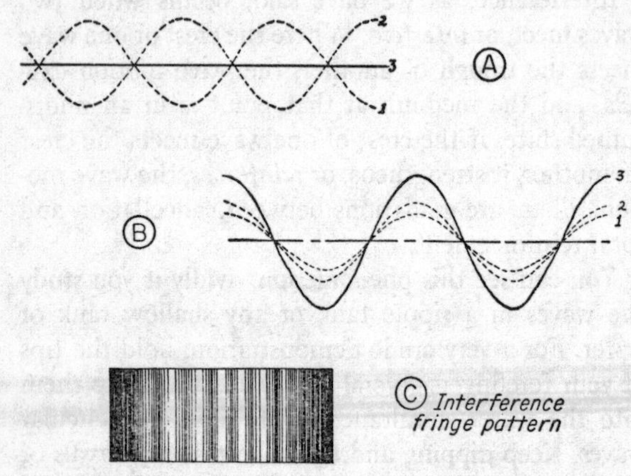

Fig. 6. INTERFERENCE. *When a wave trough meets a wave crest, they cancel each other, and the medium through which the waves are traveling remains undisturbed. The straight line of* A *passes through four such points, where the two curves intersect. When a crest meets a crest, they add to each other; the amplitude* (B) *of the wave motion increases, producing in water a higher wave or in light a band of greater intensity. In* C *you see the image produced on a screen by light that has passed through two parallel slits. Constructive interference (addition of crest to crest) produced the bright regions, destructive interference (cancellation of crest and trough) the dark ones.*

strated in 1803 by Thomas Young in a brilliant exposition that fully supported the wave theory but aroused its opponents to near fury. Young was a sort of universal genius, a prodigy at two, an accomplished linguist in boyhood, a musician, mathematician, successful physician, archeologist, decipherer of hieroglyphics, artist, philosopher, anatomist, and man of the world.

In his experiment, performed before the Royal Society of London, he allowed light of one color from a distant source to pass through two tiny holes close together in one screen and fall on another screen. The patches of light on the second screen overlapped and produced fine bands, alternately light and dark. The experiment demonstrated that light, and light alone, could produce darkness, the alternate dark bands in the image on the screen. In his explanation he showed that the light bands on the screen occurred when the waves from the two holes traveled exactly the same distance to the screen, or distances that differed by whole numbers of wavelengths—in other words, with crests added to crests in phase. On the other hand, the dark bands occurred where the wave paths differed in length by half wavelengths—that is to say, where crest was adding to trough and causing cancellation. From this it becomes plain that if in Michelson's projected experiment the two waves returned at the same instant, neither having met an obstacle on the way, no interference fringe system would show up.

What Michelson planned may not have seemed a formidable experiment. Yet it was, for light is the fastest thing in the universe. At best the differences in speed of the two beams would be extremely minute. The earth in its orbit crawls along at a rate of only about 18 miles per second; the velocity of light is ten thousand times as great. Michelson would have to perform his experiment with the most accurate technique possible and make the most delicate observations. The slightest defect of equipment, the most minute error of manipulation, would throw his results completely off. But the magnitude of the task did not faze Michelson. Lack of self-confidence was not his failing.

In 1851 Fizeau had used the interference effect in an effort to find out whether and how much water *in motion* would influence the speed of light. He brought two beams of light into interference after passing them through two parallel tubes through which he drove water at high speed. In one tube he made the light pass in the direction of water flow and in the second tube in the opposite direction. Eight years later he tried again with a different technique. Instead of two separate beams of light, he used a single one, splitting it into two distinct pencils with a semi-transparent plate or mirror; such a mirror reflects one pencil from the light beam and transmits the other—that is, allows it to pass through. So, what started as a single beam becomes two traveling in different directions.

THE MICHELSON INTERFEROMETER

Michelson made use of both of Fizeau's techniques. What he did was improve, modify, and refine

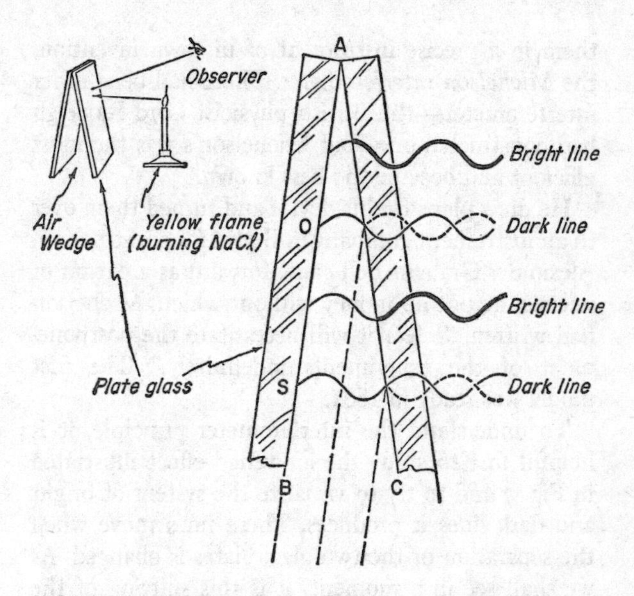

Fig. 7. INTERFERENCE BANDS *appear when you shine light on two flat glass plates separated by an air wedge. In the figures the angle of separation is exaggerated; a piece of cellophane will give enough separation. The light in this case is yellow from heated sodium. For clarity the incoming light is not shown.*

Incoming light is reflected from each side of the air wedge. The two reflected beams are either in phase and add to each other, giving a bright line, or are out of phase, cancelling each other, giving a dark band. At O and S the air wedge is just ½ and 1 wavelength thick, giving cancellation, while at the other two locations the wedge is ¼ and ¾ wavelengths, causing the two reflected waves to coincide in phase, giving the bright bands. See Plates II and III.

them in a precise instrument of his own invention, the *Michelson interferometer*. There had been other interferometers—the British physicist Lord Rayleigh had constructed one—but Michelson's was the most efficient and became the best known.

He drew plans for his device and turned them over to an instrument company in Berlin for construction. Alexander Graham Bell came forward as a patron of science; he put up money without which, Michelson had written, "I fear it will necessitate the postponement of the experiments indefinitely." The first model was ready in 1881.

To understand the interferometer principle, it is helpful first to study the air-wedge effect illustrated in Fig. 7 and to try to visualize the system of bright and dark lines it produces. These lines move when the separation of the two glass plates is changed. As we shall see in a moment, it is this shifting of the lines, or interference fringe, that the observer measures when he uses the interferometer.

In the basic Michelson interferometer (Fig. 8) a ray of light A is split in two when it falls on the glass plate P_1, whose back surface is covered with a very thin film of silver. Part of the light is reflected from this film of silver as r_1 to mirror M_1; part of it is transmitted as r_2 to mirror M_2. Plate P_2 is cut from the same piece of glass as P_1 and is therefore of exactly the same thickness; it is placed exactly parallel to P_1.

When pencil r_1 reaches mirror M_1, it already has passed through P_1 twice—the first time on its path to the silvered back surface of P_1 and the second time on its reflection from that back surface to M_1. On its

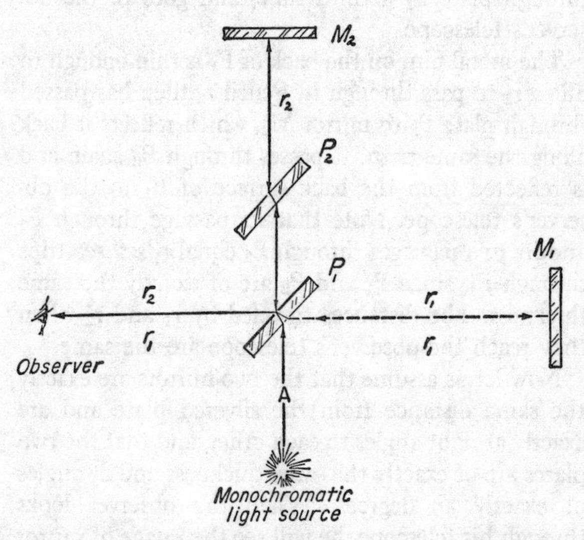

Fig. 8. THE BASIC INTERFEROMETER. *This schematic diagram illustrates the simplicity of the device, which is sensitive enough to measure light waves. Plate* P_1, *which has a thin silver coating on the rear face, reflects half the light beam* A *as ray* r_1 *and transmits the other half as ray* r_2. *The plate is at an angle of 45 degrees to beam* A. *Plate* P_2 *is of exactly the same thickness as* P_1 *and parallel to it. Mirrors* M_1 *and* M_2 *are at right angles to each other. Mirror* M_2 *can be moved with a precision screw toward* P_2 *to change the length of the path of* r_2 *and thus, as explained in the text, change the interference fringe patterns seen by the observer through his telescope.*

reflection from mirror M_1 it retraces its path, passes through plate P_1 a third time, and goes to the observer's telescope.

The metal film on the back of P_1 is thin enough to allow r_2 to pass through it. Pencil r_2 then has passed through plate P_2 to mirror M_2, which reflects it back along the same path. It passes through P_2 again and is reflected from the back surface of P_1 to the observer's telescope. Note that its passage through P_1 and its two passages through P_2 equal r_1's *three* trips through P_1, since P_1 and P_2 are of exactly the same thickness. The distances traveled by r_1 and r_2 when they reach the observer's telescope are the same.

Now let us assume that the two mirrors are exactly the same distance from the silvered plate and are exactly at right angles to each other, and that the two plates are of exactly the same thickness and at angles of exactly 45 degrees. When the observer looks through his telescope, he will see the image of mirror M_2 coinciding with the surface M_1, and there will be no system of bright and dark lines. Pencils r_1 and r_2 will arrive in phase without interference. But if all these conditions are not met, then the image of M_2 will not coincide with the surface of M_1 but will act as one of the glass plates of Fig. 7 and form a wedge with the surface of M_1. When he looks in his telescope, the observer will see the fringe system of dark lines, and if he moves the position of mirror M_2 with the precision screw provided for that purpose, the dark lines will shift their position, moving laterally across the observer's field of view. A movement of half a wavelength in the position of the mirror will cause each fringe to shift over to the position its adjacent fringe had occupied. By counting these shifts, the observer can measure the displacement of the mirror with precision.

Michelson made his first trial at the laboratory of Hermann von Helmholtz, at the University of Berlin. They had discussed the experiment at length. Helmholtz stressed the difficulties of keeping a constant temperature, but Michelson, with proper deference to his elder, demurred. "With all due respect," he wrote to Newcomb, "I think differently, for if the apparatus is surrounded with melting ice, the temperature will be as nearly constant as possible."

As had happened in his preparations for the earlier experiment on the velocity of light, this project suffered interruptions, both technical and domestic. Even though the interferometer was set on a solid-stone pier in Helmholtz's laboratory, vibrations from the Berlin traffic disturbed the observations, at night as well as in the daytime. The domestic interruption was the birth of the Michelsons' third child, Elsa. Michelson, no man for sentiment, ordinarily ignored holidays and birthdays. But a new baby girl—that was something else again. He took a break for a modest celebration.

The rejoicing over Elsa's arrival subsided, and something had to be done about the traffic vibrations. In April, Michelson had the apparatus dismantled and taken to the Astrophysical Observatory at Potsdam for another trial. There, in a hollow space in the brick pier below a large telescope, Michelson's acutely sensitive instrument finally appeared to give a clear result. (And even in this sheltered place the faint vibrations from footsteps on the pavement a block away racked Michelson's nerves as he made his observations.)

AN ERRONEOUS HYPOTHESIS

To his utter amazement, the experiment produced a zero effect. Michelson could find no drag on the transmission of light in any direction. He detected only the slightest shift in the interference fringes. Both halves of the split single beam of light were returning at virtually the same instant.

The data were almost unbelievable. The so-called ether wind had had no effect whatever on the velocity of light whether the beam was traveling with the "wind" or across it. There was only one other possible conclusion to draw—that the earth was at rest. This, of course, was preposterous.

Observations are observations; facts are facts. Reluctant as he was to do so, Michelson had to report what he had found. He recorded his findings in the August 1881 (5) issue of the *American Journal of Science* under the title "The Relative Motion of the Earth and the Luminiferous Ether." His conclusion was short and unmistakable. "The hypothesis of a *stationary* ether is erroneous," he wrote.

And where did this leave physics? Well, there was still the possibility that the earth might be dragging the ether along with it in the journey around the sun. Or, perhaps, the ether did not exist at all. Maybe the physicists had created a useful fiction to corroborate their opinions just as Mrs. Sarah Gamp in Charles Dickens' *Martin Chuzzlewit* created the imaginary Mrs. Harris to corroborate *her* opinions and stories.

Obviously, so drastic a conclusion was bound to cause controversy. The celebrated Austrian philosopher and physicist Ernst Mach, whose name has become a household word in this age of jet flight and supersonic Mach numbers, was among those who refused thenceforth to accept the reality of the ether. Lord Kelvin, the eminent English authority, who always demanded a mechanical model of any theory of nature, stuck to his belief in the ether. Sir Oliver Lodge, stanch supporter of the ether theory, rejected Michelson and continued to define the ether as "one continuous substance filling all space; which can vibrate light; which can be sheared into positive and negative electricity; which in whirls constitutes matter, and which transmits by continuity and not by impact every action and reaction of which matter is capable."

Michelson himself stayed away from the controversy. He was content to give his results the widest circulation. He demonstrated his interferometer to Cornu and other scientists in Paris and submitted his results, with corrections, for publication in the French scientific journal *Comptes Rendus*. This was the way matters stood when Michelson returned from Europe to take up his assignment as the first professor of physics of the Case School of Applied Science and, though he had no hint of it then, to form a team whose name would be linked to one of the great revolutions of human thought.

CHAPTER V

The Michelson-Morley Experiment

The Case School of Applied Science, which had opened its doors to students in 1881 and which was to become the Case Institute of Technology, occupied the old Case Homestead in Rockville Street, near Cleveland's public square. Michelson's first order of business on assuming his professorship was to set up a laboratory in an old barn on the property.

Adjacent to the Case Homestead were the grounds of Western Reserve University, which in the summer of 1882 had been moved from Hudson, Ohio. Across a road, just a few yards from Michelson's laboratory, was Western's Adelbert Hall, where a professor named Edward W. Morley worked in chemistry. Michelson and Morley soon met, and their mutual interest in science led to much talk. They traveled together to science meetings in Baltimore, Montreal, and other cities, and as they became better acquainted, their liking and respect for each other grew.

CONTRASTS AND BONDS

Outwardly, the two scientists were a study in contrast. Morley, more than fifteen years older than Michelson, came of English stock who had left the British Isles early in the seventeenth century. He was the son of a Congregationalist clergyman and had himself studied for the ministry, having been graduated in 1864 from the Andover Theological Seminary, then at Andover, Massachusetts. His career was an instance of avocation turned into vocation. Unable to find a suitable pulpit, he trained himself in chemistry, which until then had been a hobby. In 1868 Western Reserve offered him the professorship in natural philosophy and chemistry. He was deeply religious and from time to time delivered sermons at nearby churches. Indeed, it was a condition of his appointment at Western Reserve that he preach regularly in the college chapel.

Michelson, on the other hand, was anything but devout. The son of a freethinker, he grew up in a nonreligious family and never knew the ancient faith of his forefathers. All his life he remained an agnostic. The only organization even remotely associated with religion that he ever joined was the Masonic Lodge No. 21 in Washington, D.C., and he soon resigned from it. The religious instruction of his children he left to his wife. He stood in awe of the wonders of nature but could not bring himself to ascribe them to some personalized creator. Once on a starry night while he was pointing out constellations to his children, he said, "I don't care if you forget the names

Plate I. MIDSHIPMAN MICHELSON. *A photograph taken in 1873, the year of his graduation from the Naval Academy.*

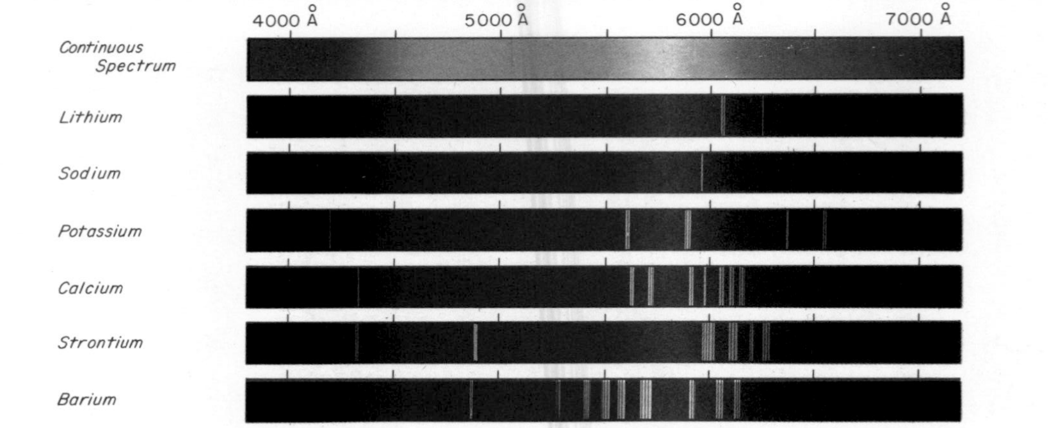

Plate II. SPECTRA. *The gradations of color in the top line constitute the* continuous spectrum *of white light. A prism or optical grating disperses white light—sunshine, for example, or the illumination from an ordinary light bulb—into this continuous spectrum. Below are the* bright-line spectra *characteristic of six metals, arranged in exact relationship to their places in the continuous spectrum. Each metal, heated to a glow, produces its characteristic spectrum as individual as a fingerprint. The wavelengths of the colors are shown at the top in angstrom units (Å); one angstrom unit equals 10^{-8} cm., or one one-hundred-millionth of a centimeter.* Note *that red has the longest wavelength, and deep violet the shortest, in this visible portion of the electromagnetic*

of the constellations, but I have no respect for people who cannot see the wonders of nature." On another occasion he wrote, "What can surpass in beauty the wonderful adaptations of nature's means to her ends and the never failing rule of law and order which governs even the most apparently irregular and complicated of her manifestations?" Yet he never accepted a deity, nor in the memories of his family and friends did he ever mention one, as the moving force of his universe of order.

Michelson was good-looking and trim, always immaculately turned out. Morley, who was casual in dress to say the least, fit the stereotype of the absent-minded professor, except that he was quick in his movements, energetic, and talkative. He let his hair grow until it curled up on his shoulders, and he wore a great bristling red mustache that straggled almost to his ears. He was married but childless.

But the professors did have things in common. Both were very musical. Michelson played the violin with skill and sensitivity, and Morley was an accomplished organist. Both were ingenious in the design of precise instruments of measurement and meticulous in construction of them. In his own way Morley was just as painstaking as Michelson and, once set on a scientific trail, just as dogged in following it to the end.

Before he met Michelson, Morley, in the routine of checking reported variations in the percentage of oxygen in air samples, embarked on a study of the relative weights of the oxygen and hydrogen composing pure water. For almost twenty years he pursued the investigation. He conducted thousands of experiments, often at his own expense. By electrolysis he analyzed innumerable samples of distilled water, and by electric sparking he combined known weights of the two elements to produce synthetic water. When he was done, he gave science values to five decimal places. The weight of a liter of oxygen he found to be 1.42900 grams and of hydrogen 0.89873 with a probable error of one part in 300,000. These weights universally were accepted as standard, as was his ratio of hydrogen to oxygen—1.0076 to 16. Morley's experiments were classic and won him an international reputation.

LIGHT THROUGH WATER IN MOTION

Lord Kelvin and Lord Rayleigh had asked Michelson to test the effect of motion on the speed of light. Michelson decided to use water as the moving medium and mentioned his plan to Morley. Morley invited him to use his laboratory. It was ideal for the project, a large basement room. Morley was not a trained physicist, but he was bright, quick, resourceful, and enthusiastic. While a student at Williams College in 1860, he had done some astronomical work. When Michelson outlined the problem to him and the apparatus he had in mind, Morley was all for starting at once. They were only getting under way when, on a morning in September 1885, Michelson appeared at the laboratory looking haggard and distraught. He was nervously exhausted, he said, and needed a long rest. He had to get away from Cleveland for at least a year. Could he prevail on Morley to finish the apparatus, go on with the experiment, and publish the results? He turned over some of the money he had received for the project and added a hundred dollars of his own.

Morley next heard from Michelson in a letter from a New York City hotel. They corresponded about the experiment. Four months later Michelson showed up unexpectedly and suggested a partnership. His health was restored sufficiently to complete the experiment. In 1886 they submitted a joint paper to the *American Journal of Science*, "Influence of Motion of the Medium on the Velocity of Light" (7). The team of Michelson and Morley had found that the "luminiferous ether" was quite unaffected by the motion of the water. They confirmed Fizeau's findings of 1851. Both Western Reserve and Stevens Institute of Technology conferred the Ph.D. degree on Michelson, his first degree, since the Naval Academy did not grant the degree of B.S. until after his time.

Now Michelson had the improved apparatus and the broader experience he had wanted for another go at the ether drift experiment, so long delayed. Morley would be in on it, too. On April 17, 1887, Morley conveyed their optimism in a letter to his father, "Michelson and I have begun a new experiment, to see if light travels with the same velocity in all directions. I have no doubt we shall get decisive results." Morley's brief description was not, of course, the whole story. Michelson and Morley were about to try to pin down the elusive ether, once and for all. From a positive result science would obtain not only a measurement of the earth's motion in its orbit relative to the ether but also of its rotation on its axis and perhaps even a method to determine the velocity of the whole solar system through space. It would be the first attempt by an American scientist to demonstrate absolute motion of the earth in space, insofar as space was identified with the ether, in an experiment with a local optical phenomenon.

THE M-M APPARATUS

The device they constructed was massive. It consisted of a stone about 5 feet square and 14 inches thick, on which were mounted four mirrors made of speculum metal (an alloy of copper, tin, and arsenic) and other equipment, including an Argand lamp. To make sure that the axis of rotation of the stone was rigorously horizontal and to prevent any errors due to vibrations, stresses, and strains, they had the stone floated in liquid mercury, which Morley had collected and purified. The mercury was poured into an annular, or ring-shaped, cast-iron trough about 0.6 inch thick; on the mercury floated a doughnut-shaped piece of wood, and the stone rested on the wood. A pivot in the center made the float concentric with the trough, which was of such dimensions that it left a clearance of less than half an inch around the float (Fig. 9). The cast-iron trough rested on a bed of cement on a low brick pier built in the form of a hollow octagon. They dug down to bedrock to set the supporting column of the interferometer; it could not be safely anchored in soil. Around the trough were sixteen equidistant markings. A wooden cover protected the whole of the optical portion—one mirror

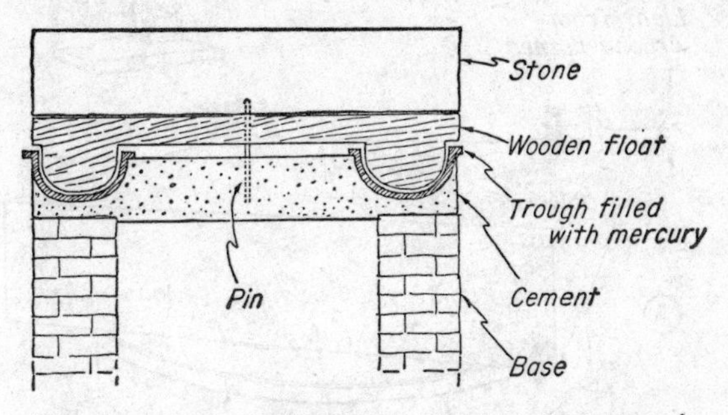

Fig. 9. MICHELSON-MORLEY APPARATUS, *seen in cross section here, was a sensitive combination of ponderous elements. The brick pier had bedrock for a footing. The large and very heavy stone rested on a wooden float that rotated on liquid mercury. The trough holding the mercury was shaped like a doughnut. Because the stone and its wooden raft were floating, they remained level.*

on each corner of the stone—from air currents and any rapid changes of temperature.

Resistance to the movement of the heavy apparatus was kept to such a minimum that only the slightest force on its circumference was required to rotate it slowly, smoothly, and continuously. The rate of rotation was held at about six minutes for one complete turn. The observer walked around the trough with the moving stone, and at intervals would stop and look through a small telescope to watch for any displacement of the interference fringe system. Such a shift would indicate a change in the velocity of light in that direction (Fig. 10).

It took several months to get this unique piece of apparatus so delicately adjusted that it could record

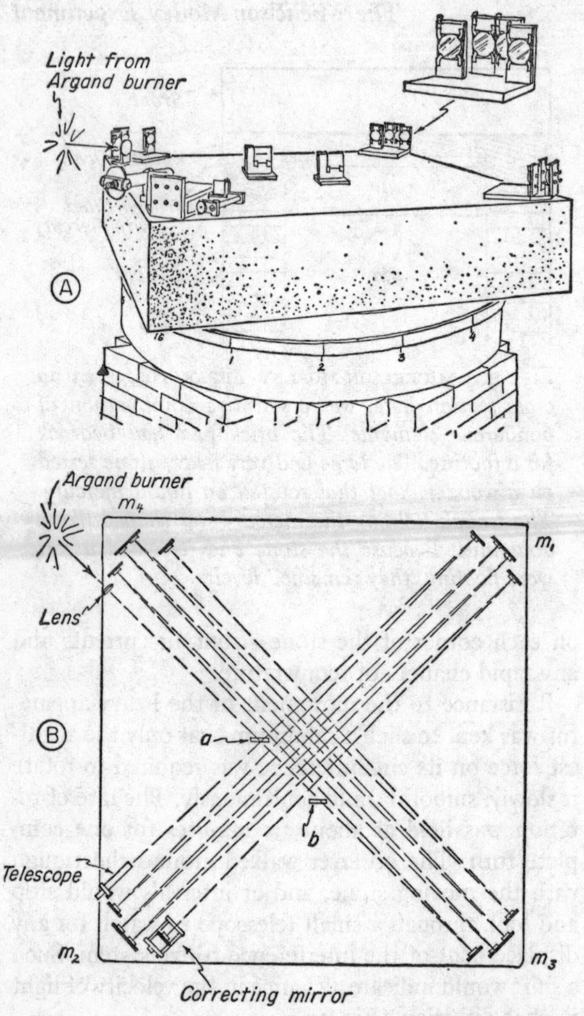

Fig. 10. INTERFEROMETER ARRANGEMENT *of Michelson-Morley apparatus is seen here. In principle it resembled the basic instrument of Fig. 8, the differences making for precision. The four mirrors gave a longer light path; the apparatus*

so tiny a measurement as the slight displacement of the fringe pattern in a single wavelength of light. Michelson and Morley took turns peering through the eyepiece of the telescope of the optical setup as they slowly pushed the stone around its course. They reasoned that in the course of a year there would be two days when the maximum effect, if indeed there was any effect, could be observed. On one day the earth would be traveling in exactly the opposite direction from its path on the other day. Hence, on one of these days the earth would be moving against an ether wind, and exactly six months later it would be rushing along with the ether wind. They made thousands of observations both at noon and at 6 P.M., day after day, for sixteen different directions, while the earth was constantly changing its position. They strained their eyes looking for interference bands and for any shift in the pattern of interference bands.

The final observations were made in July 1887. When all the data had been recorded and analyzed, and all the calculations had been made, checked, and rechecked, they had to face an obstinate fact that had destroyed a beautiful theory. No shift had been recorded of the order of magnitude demanded by the hypothesis of a stationary ether. It looked like a verdict of death to the notion of a calm ether sea. This was contrary again to all expectations. Michelson's thinking had taken kindly to the idea of an ether that could be detected. How otherwise could electromag-

---

turned precisely and was free of vibration; the massive stone retained its dimensional stability under the stresses of temperature changes; a *and* b *are the transmitting mirror and parallel plate.*

netic waves such as light waves travel? Once again a beautifully planned and executed experiment bewildered Michelson.

"THE GREATEST OF ALL NEGATIVE RESULTS"

Michelson and Morley sent their report (8) to the *American Journal of Science* for publication. It was entitled "On the Relative Motion of the Earth and the Luminiferous Ether." It also was printed in the *Philosophical Magazine* in England that year. Scientists all over the world could read the conclusion. There was no observable difference in the velocity of light in whatever direction the observer was moving. What it meant, incredible as it might appear, was that no matter how fast you ran after light you could not catch up with it. It still leaped away from you at the speed of about 186,000 miles per second. It was contrary to experience in another way. A plane flying at 400 miles per hour with a tail wind of 50 miles per hour would actually be traveling at 450 miles per hour in relation to a fixed point. A plane flying at 400 miles and bucking winds of 50 miles per hour would be slowed down to 350 miles per hour. Now, since the earth moves around the sun at about 18 miles per second, the speed of a beam of light traveling *with* the earth's orbital motion should be greater than that of a beam traveling in the *opposite* direction. Yet Michelson's experiment denied this assumption.

The British physicist and writer John D. Bernal has called the Michelson-Morley findings "the greatest of all negative results in the history of science." But the outcome did not frustrate Michelson. Even though it ruled out the existence of a *stationary* ether, the results of his experiments, wrote Michelson, "could still be accounted for by the assumption that the earth drags the ether along at nearly its full speed, so that the relative velocity between the ether and the earth at the surface is zero or very small."

Ten years after the appearance of this historic paper Michelson tested his alternative hypothesis by sending two light beams around a vertical rectangle measuring 50 by 200 feet. The results indicated that the ether was not carried along by the moving earth to any significant degree. Sir Oliver Lodge tackled the same problem in another way. He used two heavy steel disks mounted close together on a common axis and moving in opposite directions. A beam of monochromatic light was divided, one division traveling around a closed loop between the rotating disks and the other in the opposite direction around the loop. Then the two parts of the original light beam were reunited to produce interference fringes. Lodge could observe no significant change. The ether was at rest; it was stagnant.

Michelson was still not convinced of his "failure." "Since the result of the original experiment was negative, the problem is still demanding a solution," he insisted publicly. And he consoled himself with the rather unexpected observation that "the experiment is to me historically rich because it was for the solution of this problem that the interferometer was devised. I think it will be admitted," he added, "that the problem, by leading to the invention of the interferometer, more than compensated for the fact that this particular experiment gave a negative result." A strange rationalization from an "objective" scientist!

Many years later, while addressing a distinguished audience of scientists at Mount Wilson Observatory, Michelson reconsidered his relative evaluation of the ether experiment and the invention of the interferometer. He acknowledged that his assumption of the superior worth of the instrument contradicted "some other important theoretical considerations" which had convulsed the world of science. Unwittingly, Michelson, as it turned out, had supplied the raw material for one of the great structures of science —a synthesis which was to be completed overseas. This was one of the very few instances when a basic discovery was made in America for European exploitation. Almost always it was the other way around.

CHAPTER VI

Prelude to Relativity

The Michelson-Morley experiments jolted the trend of thought about light into an impasse. The whole problem—the nature of light, the reality of the ether, the meaning of *absolute motion*—was very much a matter of opinion. In all the concepts there were contradictions and anomalies. Even if there were an ether, the Michelson-Morley results might still be explained, and between 1893 and 1895 two mathematical physicists of great eminence independently suggested a way out of the embarrassment of having to accept at the same time the zero conclusion of Michelson and Morley and the existence of an ether.

George F. FitzGerald, a handsome, brilliant, bearded professor at Trinity College, Dublin, offered a staggering explanation, and Hendrik A. Lorentz, an equally gifted professor of the University of Leyden, Holland, developed the idea. What their mathematical reasoning boiled down to was this: The size of an object changes when the motion of the object is increased. In other words, a stick which is measuring the distance between two fixed points shrinks in size if that stick is moving through space along the line of its length at a very great velocity. The shrinkage —that is, the difference in length of the stick when at rest and when moving at high speed—depends upon the rate of the stick's motion. To anyone accustomed to thinking in terms of the then recognizable truths of physics, FitzGerald's theory was a sort of Mad Hatter's deduction. But these two men had arrived at the same theory from certain mathematical considerations based on the electromagnetic properties of light first proposed by Clerk Maxwell.

This unorthodox explanation disturbed the orthodox physicists. No one, they argued, had ever seen a solid rod actually shrink, no matter how fast it was traveling in the direction of its length. That is true. But FitzGerald and Lorentz were not talking about the ordinary speeds with which practical engineers and everyday physicists dealt. They were not even talking of such speeds as those of bullets. Their mathematics showed them that a speed of even 300 miles an hour would produce a shrinkage of only one million millionth of 1 per cent, a shrinkage which, of course, our instruments could not detect.

SIZE AND MASS NEAR THE SPEED OF LIGHT

When they used a theoretical speed of about half the speed of light, or about 93,000 miles per second, however, the theoretical shrinkage amounted to 13.5 per cent. As this velocity was stepped up to 90 per cent of the speed of light, the shrinkage reached almost 50 per cent. At a velocity of 99 per cent of the speed of light, our measuring instruments would dwindle to about 14 per cent of their original length. Finally, according to their calculations, when the speed of the instrument reached about 186,300 miles per second, the shrinkage would reach a theoretical 100 per cent. In other words, at this colossal speed the material stick would disappear as a result of total shrinkage and would be completely converted into its equivalent amount of energy.

Actually, an object would never shrink to zero, since the faster the motion, the heavier it becomes, and the greater its mass, the more difficult it is for it to move faster. The velocity of light acts as a limiting value. Here the measured length of an object would become zero, an inconceivable situation. Hence a speed exceeding that of light is physically impossible.

At the speed of the earth around the sun, about 18 miles per second, Michelson's interferometer would contract only one part in 200,000,000 in the direction of the earth's revolution. Now, Michelson's observations had completely ignored such a phenomenon as that expressed in the FitzGerald contraction theory. This new mathematical approach, implausible as it seemed, could explain the apparently negative result of the Michelson-Morley experiment, because the two Americans had not taken into account the shrinkage of the interferometer arm.

The effect of this shrinkage was just enough to counterbalance the slowing down of light by the theoretical ether. The run-of-the-mill physicist, not to mention the man in the street, thought the FitzGerald contraction idea thoroughly fantastic if not completely zany. Some of them were reminded of the remark of Josiah Willard Gibbs. "A mathematician," he once proposed, "may say anything he pleases, but a physicist must be at least partially sane." Nevertheless, some very serious students of theoretical physics began to examine this weird notion.

The FitzGerald-Lorentz contraction hypothesis, bold as it was and effective as it seemed in answering some of the enigmas of the ether drift experiments, was still based on the laws of the old classical physics, in that it dealt with absolute motion of particles and with possible variations in the speed of light. It shook men of science but did not throw them into retreat. Newton's classic laws of motion were still securely enthroned.

But a much more powerful shock was in store, a blow that came directly out of the results of the experiment Michelson had conjured up back in 1881, and out of a mass of new data accumulating from study of the electron, X rays, and radioactivity. J. J. Thomson at the Cavendish Laboratory of Experimental Physics, at Cambridge, England, had discovered the electron and had demonstrated that matter is electrical in nature. Studies of radium, discovered by Marie and Pierre Curie in France, had shown that electrons shot out of radioactive elements spontaneously and continuously traveled at speeds of 10,000 miles per second, far greater than ever before thought possible. In Germany in 1901, a young physicist named W. Kaufmann demonstrated experimentally that these terrifically swift electrons suffered a change in mass, and this change in mass depended upon the speed with which the electron was moving. This was an effect analogous to that described by FitzGerald. In other words, mass was not constant, as Newton had believed. And in the previous year Max Planck enunciated the concept of energy's being granular rather than continuous, transmitted in discrete bundles.

THE PUZZLE AS PUT TO EINSTEIN

The jigsaw puzzle of ether drift, velocity of light, absolute motion, variability of mass, the nature of energy, and the relationship between mass and energy had attracted a young scientist named Albert Einstein while he was working as a patent examiner in Berne, Switzerland. Einstein was born in Germany in 1879, about two years before Michelson's Potsdam experiment. He was graduated from the Technical Academy at Zurich, where students were trained to become teachers. He was an excellent pupil in mathematics and physics and, as far back as he could remember, had "a furious impulse to understand, to be informed," and to think for himself.

Einstein set out to re-examine the problem of the electrodynamics of moving bodies in terms of Maxwell's electromagnetic theory of light and the new information regarding the nature of the electron. Lorentz and his fellow physicists had made the apparently natural assumption that there was such a thing as *absolute motion.* It seemed to make sense, all right, but Einstein looked upon common sense as "a deposit of prejudice laid down in the mind prior to the age of eighteen." He saw no reason to accept this idea blindly, even though it was in harmony with the physics of the day.

Rejecting this axiom, Einstein worked out his own mathematical explanation, and in 1905 submitted the paper now known as the "Special Theory of Relativity." In this paper, published in the German *Annalen der Physik,* Einstein at twenty-six upset classical physics and revolutionized our whole conception of space and time. He reconstructed the realm of physics as radically as did Copernicus and even Newton. Two new principles were enunciated. First, said Einstein, the velocity of light is constant, the same in all directions and for all observers and independent of the motion of the source of light or the motion of the receiver. The velocity of light is a fundamental unit, basic to several principles, including the equivalence of mass and energy as expressed in the now familiar equation $E = mc^2$, where c represents the speed of light in free space. Second, Einstein banished the concept of an absolute motion. There was no possibility of ever determining absolute motion. Whether stated in one frame of reference or in any other moving with uniform motion relative to the first, the laws of physics are the same. Motions had to be referred to some definite object or framework, such as the earth, the sun, or some other body in the universe. Motion was a relative, not an absolute, phenomenon to every observer.

The great English scientist-philosopher and mathematician Sir Arthur S. Eddington once submitted an interesting analogy to explain the meaning of absolute and relative motion. Suppose, he said, we consider a man in a sealed elevator dropping through space with the accelerated motion of gravity. He is not aware of the earth or of gravitational attraction.

He takes an apple out of his pocket and extends his hand. He releases the apple. The apple remains suspended in space because, as we know, the apple is falling just as rapidly as the elevator, and can fall no faster. To the man in the moving elevator the apple *appears*, therefore, to remain motionless. He takes another apple out of his pocket and extends his hand out again at the same level but nearer his body. The second apple also remains at apparent rest but separated from the first by, let us say, a distance of two feet. After some time he notices that the two apples seem to be *closer* together although at the same height. He comes to the conclusion that the apples attract one another and hence approach each other.

To an outside observer, however, there is an entirely different explanation. The apples are dropping through space attracted by the gravitational pull of the earth. As can be seen in Fig. 11, both apples are moving downward to the center of the earth. Therefore their paths approach each other, and the distance between them gets shorter. The distance between the first position at A is greater than that at their second position at *B*. Gravitation has been the cause of this shortening of their separation rather than some unknown attraction between them as conceived by the man in the elevator.

What is motion, then? Is motion *absolute*; the same, that is, for all observers regardless of their position or motion? Or is motion *relative*, depending upon the observer's position and motion? Einstein showed that there was no such thing as absolute motion—all motion is relative motion.

Einstein also pointed out that the term "absolute"

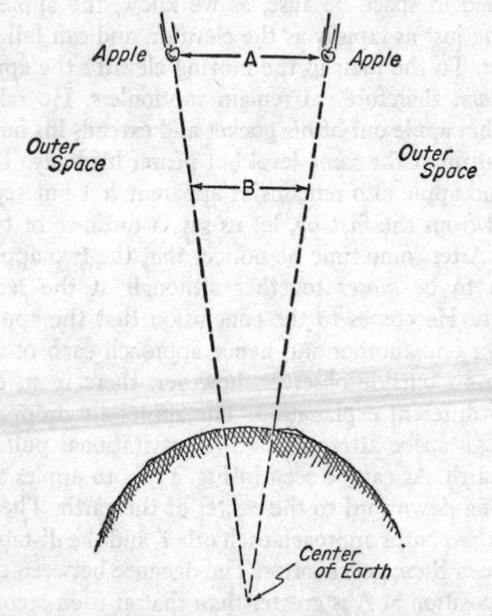

Fig. 11. GRAVITY *in the hypothetical space elevator. If you were in a closed elevator falling freely through space and let go two apples, the only movement of the apples you could detect would be their drawing closer together. An outside observer, however, would see them attracted not to each other but to the center of the earth and drawing closer to each other because their paths to the center of the earth were converging.*

could be applied to the speed of light. He showed that the speed of light, regardless of any previous notion, is one of the few unchanging constants of nature. It is the same for all observers whether they regard themselves as being at rest or in motion, and it is independent of the source of the light. An observer aboard a rocket traveling at 10,000 miles per second toward a signal light, for example, would still find that light approaching him at the same speed of 186,000 miles per second.

Einstein said that there was no reason for the existence of an ether, no need for an ether to carry light. His equations stood up in a cosmos completely devoid of any ether. The explanation he offered embodied the FitzGerald contraction concept, but he arrived at it in an entirely different way, involving revolutionary ideas of both time and space which can bend and transmit waves. Furthermore, he saw the Michelson-Morley ether drift result as perfectly correct, since no ether drift should be expected under the conditions of the experiment. Einstein developed these ideas further during the next ten years. In 1915 his "General Theory of Relativity" was published in Berlin.

Several other assumptions and predictions of Einstein's theory of relativity were later verified. For example, light carries energy and energy has mass; hence it should be attracted and bent. On May 29, 1919, two total-solar-eclipse expeditions, one on the small island of Principe off the west coast of Africa and the other in Brazil, found that light does not always travel in straight lines, as was formerly taken for granted. The British Astronomical Society's expedition sent out under Eddington photographed some stars when their light was passing close to the eclipsed sun, and observed the deflection of the light as it came close to the massive sun. The curvature agreed closely with the prediction of Einstein.

Light passing through a massive gravitational field loses energy. Its path is distorted and its wavelength shifted. Since the light is left less energetic as it moves through the field, it becomes redder. The change in color is called the gravitational red shift. Charles E. St. John at the Mount Wilson Observatory reported such a shift in the spectral lines of distant stars, and he explained that the gravitational potential existing on the surface of the sun because of the sun's enormous mass had affected the light from the stars. Walter S. Adams at the same observatory also believed he had observed a red shift in the light coming from the companion star of Sirius, and he explained it on the basis of Einstein's assumptions.

EINSTEIN AND MICHELSON

In this great upheaval in physics, the classic ether drift experiment of Michelson had been of fundamental significance. To contend, as some have done, that Einstein's Special Theory of Relativity was essentially a generalization of the Michelson experiment, and that it could not have been arrived at without the experiment, is to overstate the case. But, in a letter to the author of this book, Einstein expressed his debt to the American physicist in these words:

"It is no doubt that Michelson's experiment was

of considerable influence upon my work insofar as it strengthened my conviction concerning the validity of the principle of the special theory of relativity. On the other side I was pretty much convinced of the validity of the principle before I did know this experiment and its result. In any case, Michelson's experiment removed practically any doubt about the validity of the principle in optics, and showed that a profound change of the basic concepts of physics was inevitable."

In 1931, just before the death of Michelson, Einstein publicly attributed his theory to the experiment of Michelson.

The battle following the explosion of Einstein's relativity bombshell was epic. Many were repelled. Two of Michelson's colleagues, Forest R. Moulton and William D. Macmillan, astronomers of the University of Chicago, resisted it openly. Emile Picard, permanent secretary of the French Academy of Sciences, told one of Michelson's students as late as 1922, "On the subject of relativity I see red." On the other hand, some of the leading theoretical physicists of the world came to the defense of the theory even before experimental verification was at hand. Einstein's treatment was so logical and his mathematics so rigorous that they were compelled to accept the new reconstruction.

Michelson watched the conflict with the detachment of a very cautious scientist who insists upon waiting until the weight of evidence is in, and all sides have been heard from. In making his famous experiment, he had had no intimation of the tremendous consequences of the great revolution which Einstein's theory of relativity had caused. Michelson did not take kindly to relativity for some time and scarcely mentioned it in public. He seemed unwilling to abandon classical laws and physical concepts he had developed in a lifetime. He agreed that the mathematical equations were probably correct, for they had an uncanny power of predicting phenomena. But Einstein's reasoning was not altogether clear to him.

Michelson was not a first-rate mathematician. He was essentially an experimental physicist, and in his day the mathematical equipment of even the passing fair theoretical physicist was low by present standards. Relativity, and later the quantum theory, forced physicists to delve into mathematics more deeply. Michelson's knowledge of the necessary mathematics was hopelessly inadequate to grasp the general theory. He thought in terms of physical models rather than in abstract mathematics. But his insight into physical phenomena was powerful. He had the knack of eliminating individual terms or symbols from an involved equation until it was shorn of its complications and reduced to some simple statement. Michelson once asked Moulton for the solution of a complicated differential equation connected with an investigation of the nature of the interior of the earth. Moulton worked it out and showed it to him. At a glance, Michelson said no. He was right, and Moulton had to do it over again.

The newer physics that introduced increasing power and complexity was outside Michelson's active interest. He did not investigate thermodynamics, radioactivity, electronics, and quantum mechanics;

nor did he contribute any more to the theoretical advances that were bringing new definitions to time, space, energy, and matter. He once asked Dr. John A. Anderson, the celebrated spectroscopist of Mount Wilson Observatory, "What is the Eddington star theory?" "Matter can be condensed to about thirty thousand times the density of water," Anderson started to explain. "You mean," interjected Michelson, "to a density greater than lead?" And when Anderson nodded assent, Michelson replied, "Then there must be something wrong with the theory."

Michelson was never afraid to admit ignorance; nor was he too proud to place himself in the position of a learner. Near the end of his life he visited the physics laboratory of the University of California, where Ernest O. Lawrence, a young man of twenty-eight, was on the verge of inventing the cyclotron, or atom-smashing machine. The grand old man of physics talked with Lawrence about his project, and did not try to hide his own ignorance of the principles involved. This had a very deep effect on Lawrence. As a beginner in scientific research at Yale University, he had doubts of his capacity to turn out original work. Michelson's visit dispelled his misgivings and inspired Lawrence to stick. Afterward he remarked that if it was possible for someone to attain Michelson's "exalted eminence" without knowing everything, then maybe Lawrence himself was not as ignorant as he had imagined. Nine years later Lawrence won a Nobel Prize.

TENACITY OF THE ETHER THEORY

The ether drift experiments of 1881 and 1887 began to take on significance after FitzGerald had suggested his contraction hypothesis in 1893, and later to an even greater extent with the publication of the relativity theory in 1905. But the validity of these experiments continued to trouble some physicists. They could not make themselves accept this as the last word in the great controversy. The very slight difference in the velocity of light as occasionally observed by Michelson and Morley might be a clue to the existence of a much larger variation they had failed to detect.

One of the most skeptical and tenacious of these physicists was Dayton C. Miller, science professor at the Case Institute and authority on the quality of musical sounds. (He had also won some reputation as the owner of the largest collection of flutes in the United States, which he had turned over to the Library of Congress.) He was a first-rate physicist, a member of the National Academy of Sciences, and onetime president of the American Physical Society. Miller joined Morley in 1897 for a repetition of the ether drift experiment, and this partnership lasted for eight years.

In planning the new experiment several additional precautions were taken, and some changes in the original apparatus were made. Lord Kelvin had suggested that the material of which the apparatus was constructed might have an effect. So stone was replaced by a wooden framework of white pine. Later pine, too, was abandoned, and the setup in its final form consisted of a large steel cross, with arms 16 feet long, floating in mercury. The path length of the light was also increased for greater precision. Working in the same cellar laboratory in Cleveland, Miller and Morley finally obtained, after many trials, a figure which was much larger than the very small difference that Michelson and Morley had obtained and ascribed to known errors. This encouraged them to continue.

The following year the apparatus was removed to a shed 300 feet above Lake Erie to see whether a change in the immediate surroundings would yield any difference. This time they recorded a difference in the shifting of the fringe pattern even greater than their previous measurements had shown. At this point the Miller-Morley team broke up. With the obstinacy of the popular image of the ever toiling, ivory-towered scientist working alone, Miller refused to abandon the hunt for more conclusive evidence of an ether drift. The years rolled by. The ether still eluded him, but in 1921 and again in 1925 he was at it again. This time he had taken his apparatus to the top of Mount Wilson in California, 6000 feet above sea level. The steel frame he had used in Cleveland was replaced by a frame of concrete. Perhaps, thought Miller, the nature of steel adversely affected the result he hoped for. After thousands of observations were taken, Miller claimed a difference in velocity of six miles per second when the light path was at an angle of 90 degrees to the path of the earth's orbit around the sun. His published data, however, were difficult of interpretation, and Miller died in 1941, a disappointed man.

In 1924 a number of scientists, especially the relativist Ludwik Silberstein, urged Michelson to repeat the experiments on the effect of the earth's rotation on the velocity of light, as well as the classic Michelson-Morley determination. He agreed, but reluctantly. "My conviction is strong that we shall prove only that the earth rotates on its axis, a conclusion which I think we may be said to be sure of already." The first experiment was set up on the prairies near Clearing, Illinois, west of Chicago. The University of Chicago contributed $17,000, and Silberstein himself managed to raise an additional $491.55 to help cover the cost of the undertaking. Henry G. Gale, professor of physics at the university, and Fred Pearson, Michelson's technician, assisted in measuring the speed of light traveling through a partially exhausted 12-inch pipe welded together in the form of a rectangle measuring about 2000 feet by 100 feet (32).

The second experiment was performed with the old ether drift apparatus, which was changed to some extent. Instead of having to follow the rotation of the stone on foot, for example, the observer was mounted on the apparatus and made his observations in more comfort. A different light arrangement was also introduced. The entire equipment was moved to the well-sheltered basement of the Mount Wilson Laboratory in Pasadena, California. Francis G. Pease, astronomer and designer of optical instruments at the observatory, and Fred Pearson joined the project. The length of the light path was later increased from

53 to 85 feet and more observations were taken through the micrometer eyepiece. Again, and for the last time, no shift in interference effect was observable (34).

RECENT "TESTS" FOR THE ETHER

Others entered this still highly controversial field. Roy J. Kennedy, a fellow in physics from Johns Hopkins University, repeated Michelson's experiment in 1928 in the Norman Bridge Laboratory of the California Institute of Technology. He made a very ingenious alteration in the operation of the experiment to insure even greater precision. He read his report at a conference attended by many great scientists, including Michelson himself and Lorentz, who was now a Nobel laureate. (FitzGerald had died in 1901 at the age of fifty.)

Again no significant shift was reported, and Michelson was so impressed by the work of this young man that he complimented him: "Your work renders my own quite superfluous. I should not have undertaken it had I known you were doing it so well."

Reports of several other scientists were delivered at this conference. For example, another young physicist had stepped into the picture and did the whole business over again in the same constant-temperature basement in Pasadena. His results confirmed Kennedy's. In the meantime, the Swiss physicist Auguste Piccard, using a specially constructed small interferometer mounted in a free balloon, had obtained measurements at an elevation of about a mile and a half above the earth. The fringe system was automatically photographed on a moving film while the balloon was kept in steady rotation by small propellers. When the balloon landed and the film was carefully analyzed, there was the same result—zero.

But the search did not end here, either. Other intrepid hunters appeared with new weapons. In Britain's National Physical Laboratory, Louis Essen in 1948 unveiled a newly invented device known as a cavity resonator. It was said to be ten times as accurate as Michelson's interferometer. With it Essen got that same zero again. Finally, ten years later, at the close of 1958, a Maser oscillator was brought into action to snare the ether if it could be caught. The name Maser is the acronym for Microwave Amplification of Stimulated Emission of Radiation. The device was developed by Charles H. Townes of Columbia University.

In the cavity of the Maser is a beam of ammonia molecules which vibrate and give off radio waves. These waves travel with the same velocity as light, and so can be used as a substitute for light in the Michelson ether-drift experiment. Townes suggested that by using two Masers and turning the beam of one in the direction of the earth's motion in its orbit and the beam of the second in the opposite direction, it might be possible to find a change in output frequency if an ether wind actually existed. It was estimated that the accuracy of this measurement was of the order of one part in a thousand billion, the most precise physical experiment in history. Observations were made at the IBM Watson Scientific Research Laboratory, Columbia University. The experiment was completed and the data analyzed early in 1960, and again Michelson was vindicated. It was almost eighty years after he had made his first determination in Potsdam! And he was still right.

CHAPTER VII

A Yardstick to Endure

The versatility and capacity for work of men like Michelson (every century produces a few of them) tend to make it difficult to sort out their accomplishments in orderly array and to segregate neatly so many years of their lives for this and so many for that. At this point Michelson's experiments on the speed of light and the ether may seem to have been so arduous and so important as to preclude any other investigation. Such was not the case.

The 1887 volume of the *American Journal of Science* that reported the ether drift experiment and set the team of Michelson and Morley on the road to international fame carried another paper by the same authors. It was entitled "On a Method of Making the Wave Length of Sodium Light the Actual and Practical Standard of Length" (9). Again, this dealt with a topic that had been of concern to science for some time but had not inspired action. Several scientists had suggested that the unchanging wavelength of light might become the world's standard of length. Michelson was the one to try it.

THE BAR AT SÈVRES

A few years earlier an International Conference on Weights and Measures had been called to end the chaos of having different systems in use in different parts of the world. Representatives of thirty countries, including the United States, gathered at Sèvres, France, to discuss the problem. As a result of this conference, an International Bureau of Weights and Measures was established, and the metric system was made standard. The standard of length of the metric system is a platinum-iridium bar, about 40 inches long, which is kept at Sèvres under carefully controlled conditions in a well-guarded vault of the International Bureau of Weights and Measures. On this bar are two grooves, or scratches. The distance between these two marks measured at 0° C. and 760-mm. pressure is the accepted standard of length, the meter. This distance was supposed to represent one forty-millionth of the length of the earth's circumference measured on a meridian passing through Paris. Actually this meridian, supposed to be 40,000,000 meters, has been measured many times by different scientists, and different figures have been obtained. Nevertheless, the bar is the standard, and facsimiles of it have been made for most of the countries of the world. Exact copies of this bar are kept at the National Bureau of Standards in Washington, D.C., and from them other measuring rods and tapes are standardized.

In spite of all precautions, the original metal bar at Sèvres is subject to injury, of course, to error in measurement, and even to loss. Michelson got the bold idea that his versatile interferometer, which could measure the tiniest of distances with uncanny precision, might enable him to create a substitute. He might be able to present science with a new international standard of length based on the wavelength of some pure, single-wavelength, monochromatic light. The new standard contemplated by Michelson would remove the dangers inherent in the old one. A new meter could be reproduced at almost any place and at any time from the precise measurements the interferometer would make available to men of science throughout the world. Besides, the wavelength of a carefully chosen single monochromatic light would be unchangeable and permanent. Wrote Michelson, "In the course of millions of years the properties of the atoms which emit these radiations may change, but," he waggishly added, "probably by that time the human race will have lost interest in this problem."

NEWTON'S PRISM

The principle on which the contemplated new standard is based was discovered more than two centuries before. In 1666, when he became interested in grinding lenses, Isaac Newton, then twenty-three, undertook a simple experiment. This is how he later described it: "Having darkened my chamber and made a small hole in my window-shuts, to let in a convenient quantity of the Sun's light, I placed my prisme at its entrance, that it might thereby be refracted to the opposite wall." The sunlight was split into a spectrum of various colors. Then with another glass prism Newton reunited the different colors into the original sunlight. Thus, for the first time on record was the composition of white light demonstrated.

The results of this experiment were embodied in his first scientific paper, published in 1672 in the *Transactions of the Royal Society*. It aroused sharp controversy. The great English physicist Robert Hooke, among others, attacked Newton's theory. (Such was the bitterness of the controversy that even years after the death of Newton the poet Wolfgang von Goethe found occasion to attack the spectrum theory as "an artificial hypothesis which must disappear before exact observations and acute reasoning.") Newton, a highly sensitive man, almost stopped experimenting. "I was so persecuted with discussions arising from my publication of the theory of light," he wrote, "that I blamed my own imprudence for parting with so substantial a blessing as my quiet to run after a shadow."

Young Newton's classic experiment was explained on the basis that sunlight is composed of light of different colors, each color having its characteristic index of refraction. When sunlight strikes a prism, it is refracted twice: on entering the prism from the air and on leaving the prism into the air. The two refractions give each component color its own change of direction, different from the changes of the others. The result is the separation, or dispersion, of the colors into the rainbowlike spectrum.

According to the wave theory of light developed in the nineteenth century, each color of light may be characterized by its wavelength. Red has the longest wavelength (0.000068 cm.), and violet the shortest (0.000040 cm., or 2,500,000 wavelengths to the meter). The amount of change of direction in refraction varies with the wavelength. The shorter the wavelength, the greater the refraction. Red light with the longest wavelength of visible light bends the least, and violet the most. (It should be noted that the visible light of which we have been speaking occupies only a small portion of the spectrum of electromagnetic radiation, which varies from radio waves of very long length to gamma rays of very short length.) The difference of the speed of light in different media, coupled with the unequal bending of different wavelengths, produces the solar spectrum. As the composite sunlight reaches glass, an obstacle race, so to speak, occurs, and the colors separate.

About two hundred years after Newton's experiment, when Michelson was seven years old, a new optical instrument called the spectroscope was devised by two German professors, Robert Bunsen and Gustav R. Kirchhoff. The essential single part of this instrument was Newton's glass prism. With the invention of the spectroscope a new science was born—spectroscopy, or the science of separating the radiation from a luminous source into a spectrum of its constituent colors or wavelengths. The spectroscope reveals that some luminous bodies, such as the sun, have a continuous spectrum; incandescent vapor or gas, on the other hand, has a discontinuous, or bright-line, spectrum (Plates II and III). The heated vapor of every chemical element gives off its own characteristic colored line or set of lines depending upon the various and complex motion of the element's electrons. Each pure colored line has its own specific wavelength. Each coarse spectral line may actually be a cluster of fine lines very close together and hard to find. Some elements show a number of sharp bands of light relatively far apart and easily distinguished from one another.

SEEKING A SPECTRAL STANDARD

Analyzing the fine structure of some of the spectral lines was a difficult task calling for a high degree of experimental skill. Michelson was the first to discover that the then well-known red hydrogen line was in fact a doublet, its two components separated by about one-sixtieth the distance of the bright yellow lines of vaporized sodium.

When Michelson addressed himself to the problem of a new standard of length, the first question was, what element would be best? He started with several and finally settled on one of the distinct lines of sodium. Preliminary measurements of this line gave him his first tentative standard. The sodium standard did not satisfy him long, however, and he abandoned it, first for the green band of mercury and then (and finally) for the bright red line of cadmium.

By this time (1888) Michelson was important enough to be regarded as a distinguished citizen of his city, an honor even more rarely enjoyed by scientists in those days than it is today, and he was vice-president of the American Association for the Advancement of Science and chairman of its section on physics. But he was not happy in Cleveland. Among other things, he felt that squeezing money out of the Case Institute trustees for his department and his research was both too difficult and too tiresome. He decided to change his base of operations. At the close of school in the summer of 1889 he resigned from Case and accepted a professorship at the new Clark University at Worcester, Massachusetts.

Morley, naturally, was terribly disappointed, but he sympathized with his collaborator. "The teaching at Worcester will be much more to his mind than the teaching here," Morley wrote to his father, Sardis Morley. "They are glad to have him go from the Case School. In fact, all the professors except in chemistry will leave at the end of this year." And he closed his letter with this praise, "They certainly lose one of the first two physicists in the country." He must have been thinking of Henry A. Rowland of Johns Hopkins as the other.

At this time the University of Michigan, at Ann Arbor, offered Morley a professorship of chemistry. Michelson urged him to accept, telling him that he was "not appreciated" at Western Reserve, but Morley stayed.

When the two parted, there was an agreement that Morley was to join Michelson the following summer to continue their joint piece of research. Early in December, Michelson wrote to Morley, "I am sorry that I have to work alone at the wavelengths, but if as I hope when the time is ripe—there is a disposition to adopt the method either here or more likely in France, I shall, of course, advocate duplicate measures, in which case you will have your hands full."

Morley journeyed to Worcester only to hear that Michelson had decided to go it alone. Michelson invited Morley and his wife that winter to stay with him at Worcester "in case you come East," and he persuaded the Smithsonian Institution to lend Morley a very sensitive balance for his oxygen-hydrogen experiments. The Smithsonian had a new one made in Vienna and had it forwarded to Morley.

At Clark University, Michelson devoted almost all his time to research. He gave one lecture a week in optics, and altogether had only four graduate students in the three years that he remained in Worcester. For the most part his research still centered on the project of a new standard of length. In 1892 he reported his work to the astronomer Benjamin A. Gould, the American representative on the International Committee of Weights and Measures. At Gould's suggestion, Michelson was invited to France to continue this work in the laboratory of the International Bureau of Weights and Measures, at Sèvres. He was quite flattered, for he considered this invitation by René Benoît, the Bureau's director, an honor not only to himself but to American science.

He sailed in July of that year, taking along Frank L. O. Wadsworth, who had been one of his graduate students at Clark University. They lost no time in turning to the long and arduous undertaking that would have taxed the patience of the most dedicated of research men. Many times unexpected troubles occurred, and Michelson had to start all over again, but finally he was satisfied with his measurements of the cadmium wavelength against the platinum bar. He made his announcement: 1,553,163.5 wavelengths of the red line of the metal cadmium wave were equal to the length of the platinum-iridium standard bar at Sèvres. Michelson estimated the probable error of this figure at about one part in ten million!

The world of science had learned to believe this man. Thirteen years later three French scientists who repeated the measurement came up with a slightly different number; namely, 1,553,164.13. This very tiny difference between the two figures was equivalent to an error of only a single foot in measuring the distance between New York and Chicago. Michelson was still the great measurer, and the skillful designer of precise instruments!

The reciprocal of this precise number was adopted by the seventh General International Conference on Weights and Measures, and a new definition of the primary standard of length was established. It was "the wavelength of the red ray of light from the element cadmium equal to 6,438.4696 angstroms in dry air at 15° C. and 760-mm. pressure." (The unit angstrom, equal to 10^{-10} meters, was named for the Swedish spectroscopist Anders Ångström.) More recently, Jacob H. Wiens, an electronic engineer, and the physicist Luis W. Alvarez, both of the University of California at Berkeley, demonstrated beautifully what they consider an even superior standard. It is the wavelength of the artificial isotope of the element mercury of atomic weight 198. This isotope was created for the first time by the chief architect of the first nuclear reactor, Enrico Fermi, in 1934. It is prepared by bombarding gold (197) with neutrons. The wavelength of its sharp green line is 5460.752 angstroms. Another proposal to redefine the meter in terms of the wavelength of the line of the element krypton of atomic weight 86 was submitted to the eleventh General International Conference on Weights and Measures, and adopted in the fall of 1960. The standard is 1,650,763.73 wavelengths of the orange-red line of Kr-86. This wavelength is easily produced, and has a high degree of definition. Its accuracy is 1 part in 100 million.

MICHELSON'S MOVE TO CHICAGO

It was time for Michelson to make another move. Already, in the course of a few years, two newly established institutions of learning had selected him to head their departments of physics. Now a third was to tag him for the honor. This was destined to be the final change, for he was to remain in the post for the rest of his life.

In 1890 John D. Rockefeller's wealth made possible the creation of the University of Chicago, to be patterned to some extent on the European model. There American students could seek higher learning, where graduate and postgraduate work could be pursued in various fields. For its head a dynamic and ambitious young man, William R. Harper, was chosen. With the goal of obtaining the best talent available in this country, especially among the younger men, colleges all over the land were invaded—Harper's Raid, some called it. When the foray was over, Harper had collected for the new university some of the best-known names in the college community of the United States. Among them were Thomas C. Cham-

Plate III. PRODUCING THE SPECTRUM. *In this simple arrangement light from a common household bulb behind the slotted screen at the left passes through the prism and produces the continuous spectrum on the screen at the right. The screen on which the spectrum appears should have a dull finish. Note that violet light (shortest wavelength) bends the most, red light (longest wavelength) the least.*

Plate IV. IN HIS LAST YEAR. *A few months before his death in 1931 Michelson posed for this picture with a group of scientists at a Caltech meeting. (Left to right)* Walter S. Adams, Michelson, Walter Mayer, Albert Einstein, Max Farrand, *and* Robert A. Millikan.

berlin in geology; John M. Coulter, the botanist; Eliakim H. Moore, the mathematician; John U. Nef, the chemist; and Charles O. Whitman in zoology. The last had been a member of the faculty of Clark University, and it was not an accident that Harper became interested in Albert A. Michelson, too.

It took no subtle strategy to pry Michelson out of Clark University. He was still a young man, only thirty-eight, with fields yet to conquer. Recently the Royal Society of London had bestowed its Rumford Medal on him; his fame outside the United States was growing. He had the reputation of being bold and imaginative. In those days he was not a good man to cross; he was direct, blunt, a strong individualist—some called him impertinent—and he was disgruntled. He had had departmental appropriation troubles at Clark, as he had at Case. In one of his encounters with authority over money he told the president, G. Stanley Hall, that if he wanted to keep a first-rate physicist he would have to learn to treat him like a first-rate physicist. Michelson may have been a bit grandiose in his plans, but he was eager to develop a research department that would bring luster to American science. He welcomed Harper's invitation to join the Chicago faculty.

CHAPTER VIII

The Ultimate in Precision

Michelson stayed in Europe several months on a leave of absence from Chicago, and experts in hindsight might regard his public debut at his new home as less than auspicious. In an address at the ceremony dedicating Chicago's Ryerson Physical Laboratory in the summer of 1894, he lent his support to Lord Kelvin's appraisal of the future of science. Lord Kelvin indisputably was the grand old man of British physics but as he grew older he was inclined to turn an inhospitable face on newfangled notions. The opinion that Michelson quoted was that all the great discoveries in physics probably had been made, that its future progress probably would be confined to new instruments capable of precise measurements to the sixth decimal place! A slight miscalculation, as Michelson later was the first to admit.

Michelson's eminence was sufficient to spare him from disagreeable chores at Chicago. He was interested in research, not applied physics. "Doubtless to the lay mind," he once wrote, "and certainly to the practical man of affairs upon whom we are unfortunately dependent for support the argument of the practical value of scientific research will appeal more powerfully than the true reasons for the activities of the investigator—namely, the love of the work for its own sake."

He lectured twice a week and quizzed his students once a week on the two lectures. Some of his graduate students considered his discourses "models of fine organization, and clear and elegant exposition," but what they called his "gift of silence" bothered others —they found him too reserved. They all found his courses tough. He covered sound, electricity, and, of course, optics but stayed away from thermodynamics.

The laboratory, not the lecture hall, was the environment in which Michelson thrived, and his research in the early years at Chicago brought him international renown in yet another field of physics. His separation of the fine spectral lines of various elements in his hunt for a new standard of length had whetted an ambition to achieve still finer resolution. The spectroscope's glass prism had only a limited power to resolve complex configurations of closely packed lines. Larger prisms gave more precise resolution, but there was a better resolving apparatus.

THE FIRST DIFFRACTION GRATINGS

The existence of lines in spectra, sometimes dark, sometimes bright, but always occupying precise positions, had been known for more than a century and had been under systematic investigation since 1814. In that year a Bavarian optician named Joseph Fraunhofer counted 576 dark lines in the spectrum of sunlight (several thousand have been counted since) and designated the most prominent ones, called Fraunhofer lines, with letters of the alphabet. With diligence and delicate measurements Fraunhofer was able to associate distinct wavelengths of light with his dark lines.

As far back as 1752 the Scottish physicist Thomas Melvill had discovered that the spectra of glowing vapors and gases were quite different from the continuous rainbow-color spectrum of sunlight dispersed through a prism. The vapors and gases, which he obtained by heating various substances in hot flames, produced bright spots on the screen. Subsequent investigators let the light from the vapors and gases pass through slits, instead of the pinholes Melvill used, and they found the spectra to consist of sharp bright lines, or broad bright bands. The lines or bands produced by a specific gas or vapor were always the same and always in the same positions in the spectra.

It was discovered also that a glowing solid, unlike the incandescent vapors and gases, produced a *continuous spectrum* of rainbow colors like the spectrum of sunlight, except that the Fraunhofer lines of the sunlight spectrum were missing. In all these experiments there seemed to be some connection between the light and dark spectral lines, and it remained for the physicist Gustav R. Kirchhoff, in 1859, to make it. He managed to produce dark lines in the laboratory.

Kirchhoff let light from a glowing solid pass through a cell containing a vapor or gas, then through a slit and prism and to a screen. On the screen appeared a spectrum with dark lines. The arrangement of dark lines was always the same for a given vapor or gas. He concluded that the gas or vapor absorbed certain wavelengths of the white light passing through it. He discovered also that if the vapor through which the light passed was sodium, some of the dark lines in the spectrum occupied exactly the same positions as bright lines produced when sodium vapor was heated to incandescence and used as the source of light. Gas or vapor, he concluded, absorbed the same wavelengths, and only those wavelengths, that it would emit when heated. From this he was able to explain Fraunhofer's lines: gases in space were absorbing some of the wavelengths of sunlight.

While Fraunhofer was investigating his dark lines, he made another discovery—very fine parallel lines scratched on glass separate light into a spectrum just as a prism does. A most deft technician, Fraunhofer made a crude machine with which he managed to rule 4000 lines on a half-inch width of glass. Thus came into being the *diffraction grating,* one of physics' invaluable tools. Such a grating of carefully polished metal or aluminum-coated glass has much more resolving power than a prism, especially at the red end of the spectrum.

In the 1870s Lewis M. Rutherfurd, an amateur astronomer of New York, succeeded in constructing an engine for ruling very closely packed parallel lines. With this instrument, which incorporated a well-precisioned screw, he was able to manufacture a 2-inch grating with 35,000 lines. Its resolving power compared favorably with the best prisms in use in his day. By modern standards none of Rutherfurd's gratings, however, had uniformly ruled lines.

Then came Henry A. Rowland, son of a Pennsylvania clergyman. At the age of twenty, this young science student had written, "I intend to devote myself to science. If she gives me wealth, I will receive it as coming from a friend, but if not I shall not murmur." In 1870 he was graduated from the Rensselaer Polytechnic Institute at Troy, New York. Later, while serving as the first professor of physics at Johns Hopkins University, he set himself the task of improving the diffraction grating. He saw the immense potentialities of this versatile instrument. He and his mechanic, Theodore Schneider, built the first modern ruling engine. He succeeded in ruling between 14,000 and 20,000 parallel grooves to the inch on the surfaces of both speculum metal and concave glass. They were far more uniformly spaced than any ruled before.

With these superb gratings Rowland obtained much better resolution of light and mapped the solar spectrum more thoroughly than anyone before him had done. He then built two more ruling engines, with which he succeeded in making a 6-inch grating. This was another step forward in spectroscopy, for it was now possible to prepare a revised list of the wavelengths of light, to obtain, among other things, much higher resolution of the spectra of stars and to photograph these spectra for more careful analysis.

When in 1881 Rowland went to London and Paris to explain his new diffraction-grating technique, he kept his foreign audiences spellbound. Michelson was in Europe at the time, his mind occupied with

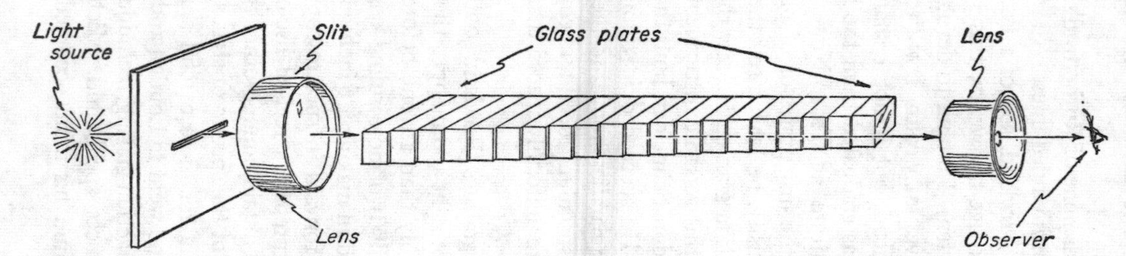

Fig. 12. ECHELON SPECTROSCOPE. *The derivation of the name of this device is apparent from the illustration. The staircaselike arrangement of glass plates "in echelon" offers paths of different length to light coming from the source at the left. Michelson invented the instrument in an effort to increase the intensity of light in certain spectra, an effect obtained only by accident with ordinary diffraction gratings. Its resolving power in this respect was superior in the order of 7.5 to 1 over the diffraction grating's.*

the ether problem. Yet Rowland's large precision diffraction gratings made a deep impression on him.

Michelson's first approach (14, 18) to the spreading of spectral lines for better resolution (and characteristically, as we shall see, he had other projects going at the same time) took a different tack from Rowland's. He looked into a recently discovered phenomenon called the Zeeman effect. Pieter Zeeman, of the University of Leyden, had found that he could spread a spectral line by putting the light source in a magnetic field. Michelson's work with the Zeeman effect began in 1895, and three years later he had invented an improved spectroscope, simple in principle but difficult to construct.

His device had no prism or diffraction grating. Instead of a single piece of glass with a grooved surface, he used a pile of glass plates of exactly the same thickness (Fig. 12). These he built up like the steps of a staircase, hence its name—the echelon *spectroscope* (19). It demonstrated once again Michelson's inventive genius.

So heavy a research program would have been all an ordinary man could handle, but Michelson, in the spring of 1899, found time to deliver the Lowell Lectures in Boston and go to Europe. The Boston lectures, established in 1839 and presented under the auspices of the Lowell Institute, were a notable annual event, and to be asked to deliver them was a mark of honor. Michelson spoke on "Light Waves and Their Uses." He also subjected Boston to sociological scrutiny. "The reputation of Bostonians for lack of cordiality," he wrote President Harper, "is pure libel."

After the lectures Michelson made a quick trip to England to receive the honorary degree of Doctor of Science from Cambridge University. On his return Harper asked him to prepare an exhibit of his optical instruments for the science exhibit of the forthcoming World's Fair in Paris. It did not interest him but, with reluctance, he assented. An interferometer, the echelon spectroscope, and his new harmonic analyzer were shipped.

This harmonic analyzer, one more proof of versatility, he developed with the help of a graduate student, Samuel W. Stratton, on money from the Bache Fund of the National Academy of Sciences. They used it in analyzing complex interference fringe patterns in which very complicated harmonic motions were involved. The machine simplified the calculations of untangling the complex patterns into combinations of simple sine curves. Harmonic analysis also is applied to the study of music, alternating currents of electricity, tide fluctuations, and weather patterns.

President Harper saw the fair in Paris in the summer of 1900 and returned an unhappy man. The Michelson apparatus had not been unpacked. He dispatched Robert A. Millikan forthwith to get the exhibit out of the boxes and on view. The University of Chicago won a Grand Prize. When Michelson, vacationing at Woods Hole, Massachusetts, heard the news, he wrote Harper: "I thank you sincerely for your own share in the work and appreciate the wisdom of your course in the matter of sending on the apparatus in the face of many obstacles—my own objections included. . . ." He was no prima donna.

A SUPER GRATING

These other preoccupations and interruptions out of the way, Michelson was able to concentrate on the design and construction of an engine to rule diffraction gratings. He would need considerable money, and he thought it proper to inform Harper.

"The science of spectroscopy," he wrote, "has accomplished a number of remarkable feats within the past decade and there appears every reason to expect that an improvement in the essential element of the spectroscope, that is, the 'grating,' will be followed by a corresponding unfolding of hitherto hidden secrets of Nature's laboratory. It is with the manufacture and improvement of such diffraction gratings that I am chiefly occupied. The process consists in the ruling of exceedingly fine lines (with a diamond point) upon an optically true metal surface—the difficulty to be overcome being the extraordinary accuracy required of a precision screw which I am having constructed in my workshop." The screw was the heart of a ruling engine. It must move the ruling point with minute exactness the tiny distance from one line to the next.

Michelson dreamed of making the University of Chicago a world center of spectroscopic activity. In the achievement of this goal he never spared himself. His research projects were undertaken most often without serious help from his graduate students, but he always kept an expert designer and instrument maker on his personal staff. He would slowly work out an idea in his head. When he was satisfied that the idea was a good one, he would make a rough sketch and call in his instrument maker. He was very clear and absolutely positive in his instructions and expected nothing short of a perfect piece of apparatus to be turned over to him.

It was 1905, six years of hard work later, when with his own engine—a modified Rowland machine—he started to rule a new grating (22). When he had completed the job in the constant-temperature room in the basement of Ryerson Physical Laboratory, he had succeeded in ruling 110,000 lines on a 6-inch surface. With such grating he was able to obtain a resolution of spectral lines equivalent to the potentiality of a prism 30 feet on a side. Monumental as was this feat, he could not stop there. He had got hold of a bear by the tail, according to Millikan, and would not let go. (His original engine was turned over to the Massachusetts Institute of Technology, where it was rebuilt in 1948.) He went on for ten years to make a second fantastic engine, and then constructed an 8-inch and then a 9.4-inch diffraction grating, which still remains the widest grating ever built by any man. It contains 117,000 lines and represents man's highest achievement of mechanical precision in this field.

Glorifying the ruling machine, he developed it to its finest precision. In the many years he spent building grating machines and spectroscopes he ran into many serious snags. Friction, vibration, warpage, creep, wear of the engine parts, changing temperature, and even the presence of dust—they all conspired to make things miserable for him and his technician. These perfectionists shouldered an almost impossible task. The grooves of their diffraction grating, almost invisible even under a microscope, had to be identical in width, depth, and contour. They had to be equally spaced and all perfectly parallel. A single wrong movement often meant weeks of repair.

"When the accumulation of difficulties," Michelson once wrote, "seemed to be insurmountable, a perfect machine was produced, the problem was considered closed, and the event celebrated with much rejoicing—only to find the next trial a failure." He came to regard these machines as having a personality. "I had almost said a feminine personality—requiring humoring, coaxing, cajoling, even threatening," he explained. "But finally one realized that the personality is that of an alert and skillful player in an intricate but fascinating game, who will take immediate advantage of the mistakes of his opponent, who 'springs' the most disconcerting surprises, who never leaves any result to chance but who nevertheless plays fair, in strict accordance with the rules he knows, and makes no allowance if you do not. When *you* learn them and play accordingly, the game progresses as it should."

Julius Pearson, who with his brother Fred worked for Michelson as a technician for a quarter of a century, recalled that Michelson often appeared not to be a hard worker. But when crisis demanded his energies, he would plod on patiently, incessantly, until he had slain the demon that bedeviled his progress. Then he would settle back again.

Michelson was not given to outward excitement over his work or to bursts of lyrical expression, but his new spectroscopic instruments elicited an almost poetic reference from him at the 1911 meeting of the American Association for the Advancement of Science.

"The messages we receive from the depths of the stellar firmament or from the electric arcs of our laboratories, come they in a millionth of a second or in hundreds of light-years, are faithful records of events of profound significance to the race. They come to us in cipher—in a language we are only beginning to understand. Our present duty is to make it possible to receive and to record such messages. When the time comes for a Kepler and a Newton to translate them we may expect marvels which will require the utmost powers of our intellect to grasp."

He lived long enough to see the beginnings of this new revelation. Through the modern high-powered resolving spectrograph, based on diffraction gratings, some of the innermost secrets of the atom have been ferreted out, and the majestic sweep of the evolution of the inanimate elements has been unfolded. It has suggested the mechanism of Nature's step-by-step build-up, from the simplest proton to the most intricate of the transuranium elements. With the diffraction grating more of the secrets of life have been disclosed. And through the revelations of such gratings astronomers at Mount Wilson and Palomar and the world's other great observatories have had glimpses of the awe-inspiring architecture of an infinite and ever expanding universe.

CHAPTER IX

The Man

Michelson was a complicated man. Had he been otherwise with his background, ambitions, and abilities, he would have been an oddity, indeed. As the son of an immigrant in an alien environment—and where could a Polish family have found stranger surroundings than in Murphy's Camp or Virginia City?—he had a rugged boyhood. The Naval Academy and the Navy gave him a vigorous training against which his intellect and creative spirit must at times have rebelled, whether he recognized the rebellious stirring or not. From persuading the President of the United States to appoint him to the Academy to inducing his university presidents to give him tools for research, his life was in considerable measure a struggle to convince "practical" people both that Michelson knew what he was doing and that Michelson's deeds were worth getting done.

A man wholly devoted to a pursuit far removed from the daily round of business of ordinary mortals and bound up in his own thoughts is likely to produce a disconcerting face to the public. Michelson was such. In company he could be delightful, but he seldom made the first move. He had the trait, usually associated with women, of liking people to seek him out. When he lunched at the Quadrangle Club of the University of Chicago, he almost always sat alone, frequently doodling with a pencil or sketching caricatures of other lunchers. If a colleague with a problem came along, Michelson unfolded, was gracious and an engaging conversationalist. But mostly he was austere, withdrawn. He never called even his closest associates by their first names. And he could be brusque, painfully so, but he was just as outspoken in his always honest appraisals of himself.

Once a Chicago colleague criticized him severely. The incident bothered the detractor's conscience, and he went to Robert A. Millikan for reassurance. Wasn't he justified in attacking Michelson? "Ask him," Millikan replied. "He'll tell you." The critic took Millikan's advice and returned, a chastened man.

"He certainly told me," he reported. But Michelson later apologized. He was "built that way," was his grudging explanation.

NO TASTE FOR ADMINISTRATION

Pedagogical demands on his time at the University of Chicago irked him when he had to be patient with those of his graduate students in whose capabilities he had no faith. He had never worked for a doctorate himself, and he grew tired of fussing with the doctorate theses submitted to him. In 1905 he asked Millikan to take the "thesis business" off his back and look after the graduate students however he saw fit. Millikan did. Michelson withdrew more and more from university administration and quit attending faculty meetings almost entirely. Administrative work took too many good researchers from their laboratories to waste time on jobs that less creative men could do. Michelson was not going to fall into that trap.

Yet he could be helpful and sympathetic. When a squabble occurred between two researchers on his staff, Samuel W. Stratton and Frank L. O. Wadsworth, Michelson went all the way to President Harper for help in straightening it out. "Nothing pertaining to the department," he told Harper, "has given me such anxiety and nothing would give me more satisfaction than to see it happily settled." Wadsworth left the university the next year, 1906, to become an engineer-inventor; Stratton five years later accepted the directorship of the National Bureau of Standards.

Michelson always was on the lookout for good men to strengthen his department, and his reputation attracted many bright young men. Some of the best stayed with him a long while. The noted astronomers George Ellery Hale and Edwin P. Hubble worked under Michelson, as did two future Nobel Prize winners, Millikan and Arthur H. Compton.

Millikan had been a fellow at Columbia University when he first met Michelson, the year Ryerson Physical Laboratory was opened. Millikan, who attended the dedication ceremony, was interested in doing some research on polarized light. When he visited Michelson's domain, he found the professor shooting beams of light from the physics building basement to the garret and back. After a chat, Millikan decided to enroll for the summer semester; he thought Michelson knew more about polarized light than anybody in the country. In the course of the summer's work Michelson gave Millikan helpful suggestions and twice went to his research laboratory to ask if he could help further. Two years later, when Millikan was engaged in research on electromagnetic waves in Göttingen, Germany, he received a cable from Michelson. It offered him an assistantship in Michelson's department at $900 a year. Millikan accepted immediately and stayed on for a quarter of a century.

OUTSIDE THE LABORATORY

In his off hours Michelson was never a team man or a spectator. Into his seventies he was physically vigorous; his figure trim. In season he bounded about the tennis court, and he walked a good deal. His other relaxations were billiards, some bridge and chess. He loved music and could lose himself completely in playing his violin.

Michelson's immersion in his work tended to drown his normal human relationships. After twenty years his marriage to Margaret Heminway ended in divorce; it had foundered on incompatibility and her inability to cope with the somewhat unconventional comings and goings of a dedicated, highly temperamental man. She married again and went to live in Nassau, the Bahamas, with their daughter Elsa. In 1900 Michelson married Miss Edna Stanton of Lake Forest, Illinois, who was eighteen years his junior.

The side of his life that was not bound to the laboratory was lived in an ivory tower. Beyond the daily newspaper he read little, except to combat insomnia with cloak-and-dagger novels. He was ignorant of business and of politics. Society held no charm for him. But his unconcern vanished when the military safety of his country was threatened. The years at Annapolis, despite the distaste for gunnery and seamanship, had conditioned his thinking.

When news of the sinking of the United States battleship *Maine*, in Havana Harbor, on February 15, 1898, reached the Chicago campus, President Harper asked Hermann E. von Holst, head of the history department, and Michelson, as an Annapolis graduate, to address the undergraduates. Von Holst counseled caution. Not so Michelson. Though colleagues reminded him that true men of science suspended judgment until all the facts were in, Michelson would have none of such shilly-shallying. He demanded an immediate declaration of war on Spain.

In World War I, twenty years later, Michelson was on the Navy Register with the rank of Lieutenant Commander in the United States Naval Reserve Force. He worked on several government projects, especially in connection with the perfection of a new optical range finder for guns—an optical telemeter, it was called. Back in 1892 he had invented an earlier model of this range finder. The new one, which could be held in one hand by the operator, became standard equipment in the United States Navy.

This work was done in connection with the newly organized National Research Council. The Council came into being after the National Academy of Sciences voted to offer its services to the government in the interest of national preparedness. The move was made in the spring of 1916 soon after the torpedoing of the French Channel steamer *Sussex*. President Woodrow Wilson accepted the offer, and an organizing committee was formed, headed by Michelson's former student George Ellery Hale. The committee recommended "that there be formed a National Research Council to bring into co-operation all existing organizations with the object of encouraging the investigation of natural phenomena, the increased use of scientific research in the development of American industries, the employment of scientific methods in strengthening the national defense, and such other applications of science as will promote the national security and welfare."

Hale tried to arouse the National Academy of Sciences to implore the government to exempt scientists from the duties of the soldier and to draft them instead, as Germany was doing at the time, for scientific work aimed at a speedy victory. England was losing some of her great scientists in the trenches and had not taken the necessary steps for the complete organization of a government department of scientific research. Some Americans opposed Hale, declaring that "scientific research cannot be organized. True research is the function only of creative imagination. No amount of organized or special stimulation or support of research can produce more or better science than the scientific genius will produce anyway."

Nevertheless, the National Research Council was finally organized in September 1916, more than half a year before the United States actually entered the war against Germany, and Michelson had a hand in its work. It was composed of leading American investigators and engineers representing the Army, Navy, Smithsonian Institution, various scientific bureaus of the government, educational institutions, research endowments, and the research divisions of industrial and manufacturing establishments. Arthur A. Noyes of the Massachusetts Institute of Technology was placed in charge of research in nitric acid and other important chemicals used in warfare. Robert A. Millikan was set to work on problems of physics. Michelson made an intensive study of the problem of more effective submarine detection. He was still in the business of waves, this time both light and sound.

AVOCATIONS: ART AND ZOOLOGY

Uncompromising patriot, vigorous athlete, committed scientist, bold experimenter—Michelson was all these and an artist, too. When he was "in the mood"—a favorite expression of his, by the way—he would take his water colors and easel to a beach, an arroyo, or into the High Sierras. As he loved his violin but rarely attended concerts, so he liked to paint but stayed away from art galleries. Once he reluctantly contributed some of his paintings to an exhibit at the University of Chicago and even let himself be talked into attending—but not for long. A woman who had been admiring his pictures coyly told him he had made a mistake in abandoning art for science. For once he masked his annoyance. He had never abandoned art, he said—only in science could art attain its loftiest expression.

It would not be stretching the point too far to say

that Michelson himself succeeded in blending art and science in a direct fashion a layman could appreciate. Among his lesser publications was a paper "On Metallic Coloring in Birds and Insects" (25), for which he did some paintings.

Michelson knew, of course, that interference and reflection of light from very thin metallic surfaces could produce color, and he did some investigating of such phenomena. With a few exceptions, he found that reflection could account for the iridescent colors of the hummingbird, certain butterflies, and a variety of beetles and insects. The one noteworthy exception, according to Michelson, was the diamond beetle, whose wings have diffraction gratings ruled as fine as 2000 lines to the inch. His paintings of these specimens were the illustrations of the paper and were reprinted, with the article, in his book *Studies in Optics*.

In 1906, in a paper read to the American Philosophical Society under the title "Form Analysis" (23), Michelson extended his thoughts on color in the insect world to the broader subject of the variety of form in the universe. He sought a unique classification for myriads of naturally symmetrical forms, and his topic embraced such widely dissimilar things as vegetables, protozoa, crystals, and liquids. He began this study with a great deal of trepidation—a singular change for the confident Michelson.

"As a recreation in the midst of more serious work," the paper began, "I have been interested in the analysis of natural forms. . . . I recognize that the subject is one whose adequate treatment would tax the best efforts of one who combined the insight of the scientist with the aesthetic appreciation of the painter, and the gift of language of the poet—and certainly I am lacking in all three—but especially in the power of adequate expression. I had hoped that my contribution would at least have the merit of originality, but I find that many able investigators have found a similar delight in this interesting field, and have expounded their ideas with a wealth of poetic imagery and of exquisite imagination such as I cannot hope to emulate."

During this elaborate classification, he stopped to make some observations on the dangers of specialized research. Said Michelson: "We tire of too great uniformity even of agreeable kinds, and the element of variety is as important in art as an occasional discord in music—its purpose being to heighten the effect of the succeeding harmony. . . . One of the great disadvantages of the modern tendency to extreme specialization in research is the loss of companionship of the sister sciences, with the attendant loss of perspective which a more general survey of the whole field of science should furnish. Should we not, therefore, utilize every opportunity which promises to further their union?"

Foreseeing the growing importance of the emerging field of crystallography, he partially answered the question himself. "The geologist, the chemist, the physicist, and the mathematician may and occasionally do meet here on the common ground of crystallography. . . . We may also include zoology and botany. . . . Nay," concluded the physicist, "Art will demand a chair at the banquet, and Music and Poetry will also grace the feast."

[illegible]

[illegible] much [illegible]
[illegible]
[illegible] the point of a quite exceptional expression! I had hoped [illegible]
[illegible]

[illegible]

CHAPTER X

The First Nobel Prize

Dr. Paul W. Merrill of Mount Wilson Observatory once remarked that Michelson had a "low p/f." P/f stood for "publication factor." On Dr. Merrill's scale a scientist who published all he knew had a p/f of 1. If he published ten times as much as he really knew his p/f was 10. Dr. Merrill rated Michelson's p/f at "less than 0.1."

Michelson had a lively sense of his own worth but never sought honors. Grandstand play did not appeal to him. Only rarely did he step out of character as on the occasion, in 1897, when he wrote to President Harper, "Though I am reluctant to trumpet my own fame, I am sure you will appreciate the recognition my work has received abroad." Even here he was asking not reward for himself but support for his department.

But no aversion to publicity or public acclaim could stave off honor for his immense contributions to science, and when honor came, he accepted it with modesty and grace. He had a degree from the University of Paris in 1895, the scarlet robe of Cambridge University in 1899, the honorary Doctor of Laws from Yale University in 1901 (another Calaveras County celebrity, Mark Twain, was honored at the same ceremony), from the Società Italiana della Scienza in 1903, and from the University of Pennsylvania in 1906, on the bicentenary of the birth of Benjamin Franklin. He was president of the American Physical Society from 1901 to 1903, and he was to become a vice-president of the American Philosophical Society and, in 1923, president of the National Academy of Sciences.

In 1907, Michelson received the greatest reward a scientist can hope for and, in a very real and practical sense, marked at the same time a turning point for American science. The Swedish Academy conferred upon him the Nobel Prize in physics. He was the first American so honored, and only one of his countrymen, Theodore Roosevelt, had received a Nobel award of any kind—the 1906 prize in peace for negotiating the end of the Russo-Japanese War.

Nobel awards in science, first made in 1901, had gone to a total of twenty-two from other countries, the first year's recipients being Wilhelm K. Roentgen of Germany, for his discovery of X rays; Jacobus van't Hoff of Holland, for work in chemical dynamics and osmotic pressure; and Emil A. von Behring of Germany, for his research in serum therapy against diphtheria.

Until Michelson the American record of achievement in pure science, apart from our accomplishments in technology, had been a modest one. There were Benjamin Franklin and Joseph Henry in electricity. The Nobel committee might have considered Henry A. Rowland for his diffraction gratings and his law of magnetic flux, but Rowland had died in 1901. Samuel P. Langley of the Smithsonian Institution was doing brilliant work in aerodynamics, and Josiah Willard Gibbs's basic contributions in physical chemistry were laying the groundwork for much of present-day chemical technology. Unfortunately, the people who could understand Gibbs were few, and his fellow Americans understood him least of all.

Michelson's work was very different from Gibbs's. His papers involved no profound mathematical discoveries. Essentially he was a superb measurer, a unique designer of precise instruments, an imaginative innovator of optical experiments. It was not the famous ether drift experiment that convinced the Swedish Academy, for Einstein's relativity, then only two years old, still aroused suspicion. (Einstein did not get the Nobel Prize until 1921 and then for his explanation of the photoelectric effect.) Michelson's citation was given in recognition of "the methods which you have discovered for exactness of measurements" and of the "investigations in spectrology which you have carried out in connection therewith." It also mentioned his standard of length and his analysis of spectral lines.

There was great rejoicing in the United States over Michelson's triumph. The press featured it on page one. The University of Chicago gave a grand banquet. More awards poured in, among them the Copley Medal of the Royal Society of London, which honored his ether drift experiment.

At the Copley Medal presentation Michelson made one of his infrequent speeches. He reminded

Europe that the American attitude toward science was changing, and he pictured his hopes for the future of science in this country. The article about his speech that appeared in *The Times* of London is worth quoting:

"The honor the Society had conferred upon him was also a recognition of the science of America. (Cheers) America was still young and had many of youth's imperfections, but every year showed progress in the high estimate in which scientific research was held. The time was already passed when an incident which he would relate was possible. An intimate friend who, after some twenty-five years, passed through Chicago and became his guest. His friend was a successful business man. He tried to entertain him in every way. But the time seemed to drag, and in despair he took his friend to see his laboratory, where he had a certain kind of engine which he thought would be interesting even to a layman. He explained the purpose of the engine to his friend, who accepted the explanation in absolute silence. When they were walking home it occurred to his friend to ask what the use of the investigation was. He had, in reply, to give him some discourse on physics, and especially on the spectroscope. His friend knew not what a spectroscope was. He explained how the spectroscope, by means of lines in the spectrum indicative of certain elements, could tell us what the various elements were in the sun and stars. Especially he drew his attention to the way in which we know by means of the spectrum that there was sodium in the sun and stars. No reaction (Laughter), or, as they said in the States, 'Nothing Doing.' (Laughter) Finally, after a long interval of silence, his friend said, 'Well, who cares if sodium is inside?' (Laughter)

"Soon this intensely utilitarian spirit would pass; and it might not be vain to hope for the date when their institutions were a little older, when they had gathered glorious names and traditions, when a thousandth part of the wealth and energy which was now busy creating more wealth and more energy might be devoted to the advancement of science and of art."

In this hope Michelson was indeed prophetic. He lived to see at least the beginning of a new realization by gifted young people that research in science offered a beautiful, a truly exciting field for a useful career. No longer were the ministry, law, medicine, engineering, and business pre-empting the brains of this country. Young people were finding new values, a deep appreciation of the creative and aesthetic satisfactions of hard, fundamental research in pure science.

The tempo of scientific progress has been steadily increasing in our country. This can be measured in a sense in the rapidly growing number of Americans who have been carrying away Nobel Prizes in science year after year since Michelson became the first recipient. Among 210 winners of the science awards since 1901, there have been 53 Americans. In the first decade after the establishment of these prizes only one went to an American; that is, to Michelson. In the next decade two Americans were chosen, in the third ten-year period three were honored, in the fourth decade nine, and in the fifth, fourteen. In the last nine years twenty-four Americans have become Nobel laureates, receiving more than half the awards made in all fields of science. Including Michelson's, seventeen awards in physics have come to Americans.

CHAPTER XI

Reaching for a Star

One day in 1914 when Michelson was lunching at the Quadrangle Club, alone as usual, Thomas C. Chamberlin, professor of geology at Chicago, stopped at his table. The geologist had a problem nagging him.

Sir George Darwin had constructed a theory of the tidal evolution of the earth-moon system, which pictured the separation of the moon torn from its mother earth; the theory assumed that the earth was a viscous body. The high temperature of the interior of the earth kept it semifluid, according to the English scientist. Lord Kelvin, on the other hand, argued that the earth because of enormous pressures existing in its center was rigid in spite of its extremely high internal temperature. These were two great names in science, yet they could not both be right. Perhaps each was somewhat in error, and the truth somewhere in between.

Theoretical speculation had not been convincing enough to satisfy the whole scientific community. What was needed was a clear-cut experiment. Some experiments involving the use of delicate pendulums had been tried, but none proved decisive. Michelson and Chamberlin talked the whole problem over in detail. They finally got around to the seemingly omnipotent interferometer. Here was an instrument that could measure the tiniest of differences in length with uncanny precision. Perhaps the solution lay here.

CHECKING THE EARTH'S CORE

With two congenial younger colleagues, Henry G. Gale, who had helped Michelson in some of his velocity-of-light experiments, and another physicist, Harvey B. Lemon, Michelson undertook a definitive experiment. Two pipes, each 502 feet long and 6 inches in diameter, were buried underground at a depth of 6 feet on the campus of the Yerkes Observatory at Lake Geneva, in Wisconsin. One pipe ran east and west, the other north and south. The ends of the pipes were closed with glass plates, and an observation chamber was built at their junction. The pipes, half filled with water, ended in concrete-lined pits 10 feet deep and 8 feet square, in which the observations were made. Interferometers were installed at either end of each of the two pipes.

Just as the moon and the sun pull the waters on the surface of the earth and produce the familiar tides, so, Michelson reasoned, they ought also attract the water of tiny artificial "seas" in these two pipes. The nature of the interior of the earth would affect the extent of the gravitational pull, whether the interior was solid or molten. If the earth had no rigidity at all—that is, if it were a fluid—no miniature tide would be produced, for the moon's attraction would distort the earth's shape as much as it would distort the shape of the miniature seas. If, on the other hand, the earth were perfectly rigid, the tiny tides of the water in the pipes would follow a definitely calculable pattern.

A clockwork device installed in the equipment could be set to draw a moving-picture film showing the water level at the rate of about one inch an hour. This would provide a record of any rise or fall of the surface of the water in the pipes. Michelson's interferometers were employed at the same time to measure these extremely minute distances. Their optical fringe systems were examined at various hours of the day and night over long periods during the four seasons.

It was a delicate and tedious job. Things went wrong, frequent repairs had to be made, many modifications had to be improvised, and a mountain of data collected. Finally, the highly involved tidal computations essential to a complete analysis of the recorded information were turned over to Forest R. Moulton and his computing staff. When the analysis was completed, the results seemed to indicate that the viscous yielding of the earth was extremely slight. The tides observed in the tubes turned out to be infinitesimal, just a few thousandths of an inch at their maximum point. The earth appeared to have about the same elasticity, rigidity, and viscosity as steel. The interior of the earth must, therefore, be a huge chunk of iron.*

MEASURING A GIANT STAR

To the layman there was nothing spectacular about this piece of research. The results were published (28) by Michelson and Gale in 1919 in four different scientific journals here and abroad, and were promptly forgotten. But near the close of the following year every man, woman, and child who read a newspaper anywhere in the United States was treated to a rare thrill. On December 30, 1920, the New York *Times* carried the story on its entire front page. The headline read, "Giant Star Equal to 27,000,000 Suns Like Ours, measured by Michelson . . . a great triumph of science." A large drawing showed the relative size of this colossus of the sky. And the next day the paper printed a long editorial about this feat of science. Michelson was the first in history to measure the angular diameter of a distant star.

When the news was flashed that the giant star Betelgeuse (Alpha Orionis), located in the shoulder of the constellation Orion, a tiny spot glowing with a red light about 200 light-years away in the vastness of space, was approximately 240,000,000 miles in diameter, there must have been few indeed who did not feel some awe. Here was a star with a diameter more than 250 times greater than that of our own

* For a fuller discussion of this subject, see *How Old Is the Earth?* by Patrick M. Hurley, Science Study Series, Doubleday Anchor Books, 1959.

sun and 1200 times brighter. The sun with a diameter under a million miles was a dwarf in comparison. Twenty-seven millions of our own sun could be fitted comfortably inside the body of Betelgeuse! Its sphere is almost large enough to pack within its borders the entire orbit of the planet Mars as it circles the sun.

This was really something big, something new, something the layman could understand and discuss without benefit of mathematics or ability to use abstractions. It was concrete, simple. Newspapers had shown diagrams of the relative size of Betelgeuse. Seldom did a scientific achievement take hold of popular interest and excitement as did this spectacular experiment. Michelson was the man of the hour.

In one majestic flight he had leaped from the spectral analysis of the innermost recesses of the tiniest of atoms to the giant stars of the dark, distant corridors of outermost space. This, however, was not his first venture into the field of astronomy. Thirty years before, while he was still on the staff of Clark University, he had published a paper in the *Philosophical Magazine* (11) which described some observations of a double star named Capella; he had used essentially the same method he had employed on Betelgeuse. The two members of Capella were too close to each other for clear resolution by even the most penetrating telescope on earth. Michelson had put into play his famous interferometer, with which he hoped to measure "the apparent size of telescopic objects such as planetoids, satellites, and *possibly stars.*" Then the following year he took his equipment to the Lick Observatory on the top of Mount Hamilton, California, and with the aid of his assistant, Frank L. O. Wadsworth, and Professor William W. Campbell, actually measured Jupiter's satellites (12).

The work on Betelgeuse started at the invitation of George Ellery Hale, who had left the University of Chicago in 1905 for California. Hale first met Michelson in 1888 at a science meeting in Cleveland, where Michelson described his new interferometer. Later, Hale became a member of the staff of the University of Chicago and remained there for thirteen years. He had many opportunities to talk to Michelson and watch him at work. He felt certain that this man could do the impossible. Hale had founded, and was now director of, the Mount Wilson Solar Observatory. Mount Wilson had the most powerful telescope in the world at that time, a 100-inch instrument. But even this colossus was powerless to measure the diameter of a single star. Stars appear as points of light. No star has a disk large enough to be seen. Because of the great distances of these bodies from the earth, it is impossible to magnify them so that they will appear as measurable disks. It was calculated that a lens or mirror of about 20 feet aperture would be needed to do this.

THE INTERFEROMETER AND TELESCOPES

Hale persuaded Michelson to try the experiment. The war intervened, but in 1919 the work was resumed. After some preliminary tests with the 40-inch refracting telescope of the Yerkes Observatory at Lake Geneva, in Wisconsin, the method was tested by Michelson and Francis G. Pease during the summer of 1920 on both the 60-inch telescope and the 100-inch telescope of the Mount Wilson Observatory. The telescope's mirror was covered with an opaque cap containing two adjustable slits and the telescope was turned to the star to be measured. A diffraction fringe system appeared at the eyepiece of the observer, produced by the interference of the two pencils of light. When the slits were now moved, the texture of the image slowly changed until a distance between them was found at which the fringes disappeared. At this point

$$\alpha = \frac{1.22 \text{ wavelength of light of the star}}{\text{distance between the 2 movable mirrors}}$$

where α is the angle subtended at the telescope by the diameter of the disk. From the then accepted distance of the star from the earth, its actual linear diameter in miles could be calculated.

The plan to increase the resolving power of the 100-inch telescope with the aid of the Michelson interferometer was then improved (Fig. 13). Two small adjustable mirrors which could be separated a distance of 20 feet were used. A steel girder more than 20 feet long was placed transverse to the tube of the telescope. The two movable plane mirrors, one placed at each end of the 20-foot girder and mounted at 45 degrees, would receive the light from the distant star. This light would then be reflected by other mirrors to the focus of the telescope's mirror. The 45-degree mirrors would be moved apart. Again the distance between these mirrors when the interference fringes disappeared gave the angular diameter of the star.

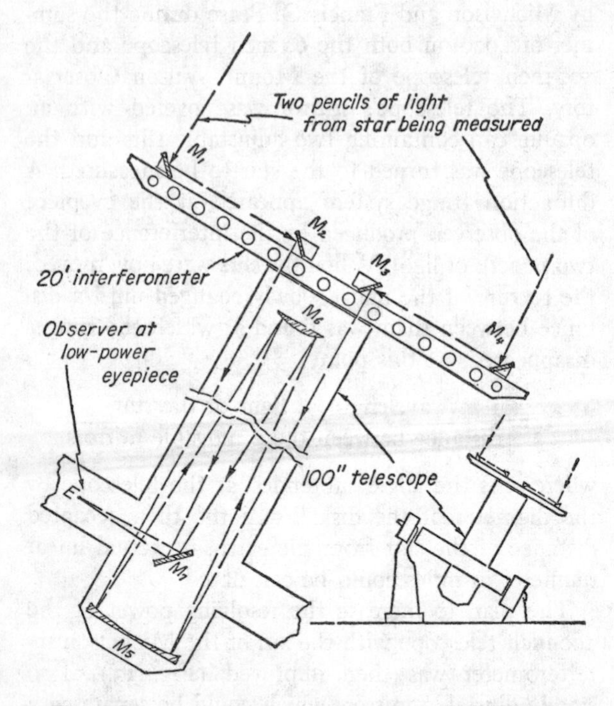

Fig. 13. STELLAR INTERFEROMETER. *This diagram shows the mounting of a Michelson interferometer on the 100-inch telescope at Mount Wilson. With this apparatus Francis G. Pease measured the diameter of Betelgeuse in 1920. The mirrors* M_1 *and* M_4 *reflected pencils of light from the star to mirrors* M_2 *and* M_3*, which reflected them through the telescope's optical system. The observer at* E *saw double slit interference fringes like the teeth of a comb. Increasing the separation of* M_1 *and* M_4 *changed the fringe pattern. At the separation where the*

On December 13, 1920, Pease obtained his first conclusive measurement. He found the angular diameter of Betelgeuse to be 0.047 seconds of arc, and from this he calculated its diameter. Ten days later he made another determination, and on December 23 wired the results of his last measurement to Michelson, who was attending a joint meeting of the American Physical Society and the American Association for the Advancement of Science. Michelson, elated, read the results the following day to the assembled scientists. The Royal Astronomical Society of England recognized the achievement by presenting Michelson its gold medal.

Pease then repeated the experiment by pointing the 100-inch telescope capped by Michelson's interferometer to other stars in the heavens. Arcturus, Aldebaran, and Antares showed their faces, and their diameters, too, were revealed for the first time. They were all shown to be giant stars with linear diameters of about 20 million, 30 million, and 400 million miles, respectively. These original figures obtained about four decades ago have held up rather well. Betelgeuse, a variable, pulsating star, varies in diameter between 360 and 500 million miles. Today's most reliable figures for Arcturus, Aldebaran, and Antares are 30 million, 35 million, and 410 million miles.

---

pattern disappeared altogether in a blur of light, the angular diameter of the star could be calculated. The formula is $\alpha = \frac{1.22\lambda}{s}$, *where* λ *is the mean wavelength of the light from the star,* s *is the separation of* M_1 *and* M_4, *and* α *is the angle subtended by the star diameter.*

Pease and Hale later set to work to design an even larger interferometer. With this new 54-foot stellar interferometer they hoped to measure other stars, fainter and smaller than those already explored.

By now Albert Michelson had reached seventy. This was the usual age of retirement for members of the faculty of the University of Chicago. The board of trustees of the institution was delighted, however, to hold on to him as long as possible. They reappointed him a year at a time for as long as he wished at an annual salary of $8000.

CHAPTER XII

Full Circle

Not often is a man in his seventies called upon to return to the work of his youth because the world still regards him as the person most likely to be able to improve what was a thoroughly good job in the first place. Michelson enjoyed this enviable experience.

In 1923 George Ellery Hale of Mount Wilson Observatory asked Michelson to go to Pasadena and make another determination of the speed of light. Michelson was delighted. For a long time he had wanted the chance to improve on his great work of 1882. He lost no time getting to California and setting up headquarters at the foot of Mount Wilson.

Plans were carefully laid. Two sites were chosen. One was the familiar top of Mount Wilson and the other the peak of Mount San Antonio, or "Old Baldy," 10,080 feet above sea level and 22 miles away. The United States Coast and Geodetic Survey was called in to lay out a base line in the San Gabriel Valley for an accurate measurement of the distance between the two reflecting surfaces—a rotating prism-mirror on Mount Wilson and a fixed mirror on Mount San Antonio. The probable error in the surveyed base line was one part in about seven million, or a fraction of an inch in the 22 miles.

A rotating prism of nickel-steel with eight mirror surfaces polished true to one part in a million was made by Elmer A. Sperry, an engineer-and-inventor friend of Michelson, president of the Sperry Gyroscope Company of Brooklyn, New York. Several other glass and steel prisms were also prepared for the experiment. The octagonal high-speed rotor could make 528 turns a second. It was driven by an air blast, and its speed was regulated by an electric tuning fork as in his earlier experiments. (A tuning fork has other applications besides that of a standard of pitch employed by musicians. It can very accurately mark off short and equal intervals of time. Such an instrument with the required frequency can be constructed and kept vibrating by means of an electric current similar to that of a doorbell.)

Sperry had also recently perfected a high-intensity arc searchlight for military purposes and offered it to his friend. Preston R. Bassett, research engineer in charge of this searchlight project and later president of the company, prepared a special arc-lamp mechanism for the light experiment and personally took it to California in the summer of 1924. Fred Pearson went out from Chicago to assist.

MOUNTAINTOP MEASUREMENTS OF THE SPEED OF LIGHT

Like a commander on the quarterdeck, Michelson enthusiastically directed every detail of the operation.

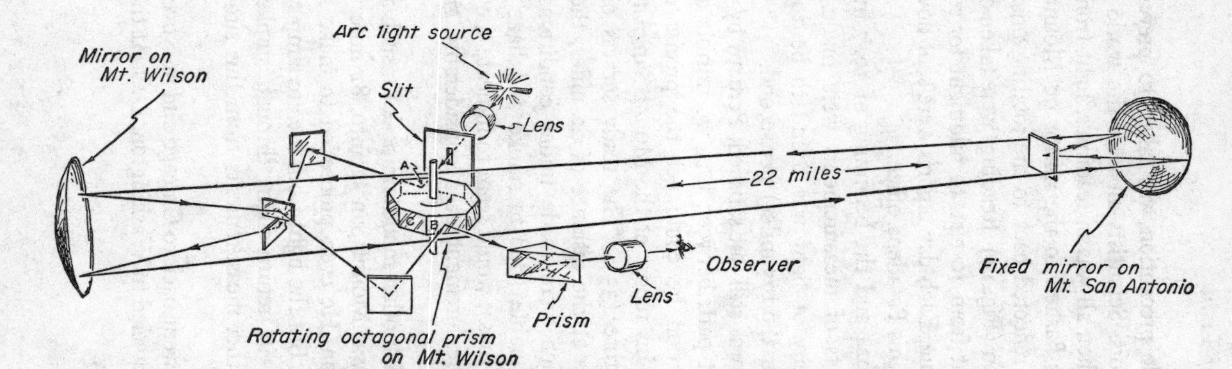

Fig. 14. MANY REFINEMENTS of Michelson's original method of measuring the speed of light are to be seen in this diagram of his apparatus of the late 1920s, but the principle was essentially the same. The main change was in the length of light path.

Every possible precaution was taken to prevent or minimize errors. Scientists all over the world were watching. When all was in readiness, light from the arc lamp was flashed to the mirror on Mount San Antonio and reflected back to the rotating prism on Mount Wilson (Fig. 14). Readings were taken on every clear night from 10 P.M. to midnight for several weeks at a time. Each day reports were sent down to Michelson at his Pasadena office.

Between 1924 and the beginning of 1927 five independent sets of measurements were made. The average velocity of light was found to be 299,798 kilometers (or 186,175 miles) per second.

Michelson was still not satisfied. Perhaps by using a longer light path between the two mirrors and a different location he could get the precise determination. In his report of the Mount San Antonio project he wrote (33), "The ready success of the measurements at the distance of 22 miles, the majority of which were made under conditions not the most favorable (due to smoke and haze from nearby forest fires), would seem to indicate the feasibility of a measurement at a considerably greater distance."

He selected another mountain peak for such an experiment. It was Mount San Jacinto, 82 miles from Mount Wilson. He even proceeded to make a preliminary trial. But the light from the arc lamp was so enfeebled on its return flight through smoke and haze that further measurements from this site were given up.

Michelson went back to Chicago and in November of that year traveled to Washington, D.C. At the National Bureau of Standards a gala scientific conference was held. It had been organized by the Optical Society of America to commemorate the fiftieth anniversary of the publication of Michelson's first paper on light in 1878, and in appreciation of his preeminent contributions to optics over half a century. It was known as the Michelson Meeting; Michelson, of course, was the guest of honor.

THE FINAL TRY

The following year, at the age of seventy-seven, Michelson suffered a serious cerebral hemorrhage. He resigned his post at the university, and worked to regain his old vigor by sketching, painting, and walking. It was not easy. But always he kept thinking of getting back to his researches on light. He called upon light to give him life for a new determination. He went back more than half a century to where he had started. He wanted to capture the velocity of light without the obstruction of haze or smoke or even the pure, gossamer-thin atmosphere itself. He wanted to do the experiment with the light beams traveling through almost empty space, through a near-perfect vacuum, if possible.

At this crucial moment of his life Michelson was invited back to Pasadena. "Hale said I could have Mount Wilson and Caltech," Michelson said later. "The temptation was too great. So I came." All the necessary funds and facilities for a new experiment were made available to him. The Rockefeller Foundation provided $30,000, the Carnegie Corporation $27,500, and the University of Chicago $10,000.

A site for the grand attempt was selected on the Irvine Ranch near Santa Ana, in southern California. The United States Coast and Geodetic Survey again surveyed the base line over which the new measurements were to be made. A huge tube costing $50,000 was constructed. It was made of 14-gauge galvanized Armco steel sheets rolled and corrugated. The 60-foot culvert pipe sections, each 3 feet in diameter, were brought together, their seams riveted and soldered to make a mile-long single tube. Four manholes gave access to its interior, one at each end, and two others in the main section of the pipe. The Sperry Gyroscope Company again was happy to supply rotating mirrors of steel with 8, 16, and 32 facets. A well-annealed optical-glass mirror with 32 facets was also furnished.

Special pumps working day and night evacuated the sealed tube until the air pressure was down to half a millimeter of mercury, compared with the normal 760 mm. of air pressure outside the tube. Light from an arc lamp was to be shot between the mirrors. In multiple reflections the light path was to be increased to about 10 miles. For the first time in history the speed of light in an almost perfect vacuum was to be recorded.

In the meanwhile, Michelson's health was not improving very much. He was never really well enough again to make the actual measurements himself. Francis G. Pease and Fred Pearson once again co-operated in taking measurements and correlating the data. Through all 1930 and part of the next year hundreds of observations were made. Michelson directed from his sickbed; he could not possibly have handled the many emergency problems that cropped up at the site of the experiment. Every time something went wrong with the equipment, air had to be admitted to the pipe so that the men could go in and make repairs. Then they had to wait forty-eight hours while the tube was evacuated again. Heat waves distorted the light image; most of the work had to be done in the cool of the night.

Early in 1931 the experimenters were still grappling with their problem. Michelson seemed for a while to be recovering from the stroke. Einstein was in Pasadena at a scientific conference, and other famous scientists from many parts of the world were in town for a banquet, on the fifteenth of January, to honor Dr. and Mrs. Einstein. Two hundred members of Caltech's Associates were the hosts. Michelson, of course, was invited, and he was very happy to be well enough to attend the grand occasion in the new and beautiful Athenaeum.

Einstein made a little speech. Seated near him were Michelson, Millikan, Hale, and other eminent men of science. "I have come among men," began Einstein, "who for many years have been true comrades with me in my labors." Then, turning to the measurer of light, he continued, "You, my honored Dr. Michelson, began with this work when I was only a little youngster, hardly three feet high. It was you who led the physicists into new paths, and through your marvelous experimental work paved the way for the development of the Theory of Relativity. You uncovered an insidious defect in the ether theory of light, as it then existed, and stimulated the ideas of H. A. Lorentz and FitzGerald, out of which the Special Theory of Relativity developed. Without your work this theory would today be scarcely more than an interesting speculation; it was your verifications which first set the theory on a real basis."

Michelson was deeply moved. There could be no higher praise for any man. He rose to acknowledge this generous praise. He seldom made speeches and when he did they were short and to the point. This was to be no exception. He thanked Einstein for his public acknowledgment of his work and that of his partner, Edward Morley, who had died eight years before. Michelson never failed to give credit to his collaborators and assistants.

This was Michelson's last public appearance. He tried to go back to his work again. On March 1, however, he could not leave his bed. A creeping paralysis had set in. As he grew weaker and weaker the data from Santa Ana kept coming in. With his last strength he called Pease to his bedside. Slowly but distinctly he dictated the introduction for the paper that was to describe the final results of his final experiment. This report was to be sent to the *Astrophysical Journal* for eventual publication.

Michelson's condition continued to worsen, but he refused to admit his very serious illness. "My health continues to improve," he wrote optimistically, but forty-eight hours later he fell into a coma. Mrs. Michelson, one of his daughters, and two nurses remained at his bedside. Pease and Pearson joined them. At twelve fifty-five on Saturday afternoon, May 9, he died quietly in his sleep.

The pastor of the local Union Liberal church held a short and very simple service in the parlor of Michelson's home in Pasadena. At the widow's request no press notice was released until after the funeral. Only his wife, Edna, their three daughters, Madeleine, Dorothy, and Beatrice, and a few other members of the family, and a small number of very close friends were present. Millikan, Hale, and Hubble carried the coffin to the hearse. His body was cremated and his ashes scattered. This was Michelson's wish.

Scientists throughout the world honored his work. Einstein, who received the news while he was lecturing at Oxford, England, said, "Dr. Michelson was one of the greatest artists in the world of scientific experimentation."

Three of Michelson's closest associates at the University of Chicago, Forest Ray Moulton, Henry G. Gale, and Harvey B. Lemon, who had known him for a quarter of a century, summed up his achievement:

"His life was a magnificent exhibition of singleness of purpose, unruffled by the winds of favor or disfavor. Even the cosmic forces of hate, love, jealousy, envy, and ambition seemed to move him little. Possessed of an extraordinary indifference to people in general because of his absorption in his scientific pursuits, he, nevertheless, had the capacity of making and cherishing a few devoted friends. . . . The dominant note of his life was that he was moved and inspired by scientific achievement, by the esthetic enjoyment his work gave him. . . . He was unhurried and unfretful. He never feared that science or mankind was at a crucial turning point. He never trembled at the brink of a great discovery. . . . He was gentle and wholly without affectation like a sea on a summer's day, serene, illimitable, unfathomable. . . . Such a personality can be felt, not analyzed. Of Michelson one knew only the surface, little more, one sensed much that could not be fathomed. Very few people ever knew him intimately."

Work with the mile-long vacuum tube on the Irvine Ranch continued for the best part of another two years after Michelson's death. The Long Beach earthquake of 1933 wrecked the installation, but the project was already completed. In all, 2885 determinations were made. The final mean figure for the velocity of light in a vacuum was found to be 299,774 kilometers per second, or about 14 miles less than the result of the previous mountaintop experiments. The figure 299,792.5 kilometers has been adopted by the International Union of Geodesy and Geophysics (for surveying purposes) and by the International Scientific Radio Union (for radio work). This value is well within the limits of experimental error of Michelson's figure, which is still probably the most reliable one ever obtained.

When the report was finally published, its title sounded the same theme as that of Dr. Michelson's first paper when he was Ensign Michelson of the United States Navy, more than half a century before. "On a Method of Measuring the Velocity of Light" (35) was the completion of an epic contribution to physical science.

THE CONTINUING SEARCH

There is no last word or ultimate solution in the adventure of scientific research. Could Michelson return today to the great scientific laboratories of the world, he would find that the same problems that he and other men of science had set out to solve are still vexing researchers. Firmly established ideas are toppled, replaced, expanded, or improved. Newton's contributions were modified by Einstein. Darwin's mansion of evolution was refurbished and enlarged by Thomas Hunt Morgan and his school of geneticists. And the velocity of light—that constant that Michelson himself seemed to have pinned down once and for all—how does it fare today? Doubts still hover about it. Other men with new techniques and new tools have attacked it anew. Research teams both at Harvard University and in Germany, using a so-called electronic light chopper, in 1939 obtained slightly different figures for the speed of light—299,798 kilometers per second in this country, and 299,799 kilometers per second in Europe. Two years later, scientists at the National Bureau of Standards clocked a speed of 299,795 kilometers. In 1951 Commander Carl I. Aslakson of the United States Coast and Geodetic Survey, while testing a radar system, obtained the figure 299,805 per second. Then, three years later, a British team again recorded this same figure.

A few scientists in the field have expressed their suspicion that the speed of light may not be constant after all. They say it has actually changed, for pre-

World War II measurements and post-World War II determinations, separated by a decade of time, have shown a difference of about 16 kilometers (or 10 miles) per second. According to Professor J. H. Rush of Texas Technological College, "This is not to be taken lightly as inescapable errors of technique." The search should go on, Rush insists. "New measurements may lead to a new discovery." And the hunt does continue.

And where do we stand on the reality and nature of the "ether"? In 1899 in his Lowell Lectures, Michelson had touched on this topic. "Suppose," he had said at that time, "that an ether strain corresponds to an electric charge, an ether displacement to the electric current, ether vortices to the atoms—if we continue these suppositions we arrive at what may be one of the grandest generalizations of modern science, namely, that all the phenomena of the physical universe are only different manifestations of the various modes of motion of one all-pervading substance—the ether. The day seems not too far distant when the converging lines from many apparently remote regions of thought will meet on some common ground. Then the nature of the atom and the forces called into play in their chemical union, the interactions between these atoms and the non-differentiated ether as manifested in the phenomenon of light and electricity, the structure of the molecule, the explanation of cohesion, elasticity and gravitation—all these will be marshalled into a single compact and consistent body of scientific knowledge."

Today, more than sixty years later, this hope has still not been realized. Light and all other electromagnetic radiation still remain privileged forces which seem to require no transmitting medium at all. The ether seems to have given up the ghost, thanks in no small measure to the genius of Michelson.

Epilogue

Seventeen years after his death the United States Navy paid rare honor to one of its sons. A $7,000,000 laboratory for basic and applied research in physics and allied sciences was named for Albert Abraham Michelson. It is at the U. S. Naval Ordnance Test Station, Inyokern, China Lake, California, in the northern part of the Mojave Desert. In the main lobby of the Michelson Laboratory is the Michelson Museum, filled with large display cases containing medals, awards, documents, and letters that relate to the life and work of this graduate of the Naval Academy. Original equipment and models of apparatus constructed according to his design and under his direction are also on view. Among them are the original harmonic analyzer, a diffraction grating, vertical and parallel interferometers, models of his ruling machine, the 100-inch telescope with Michelson's stellar interferometer attached, and the Michelson-Morley ether drift equipment. Here are works of art and science to excite the imagination, to stimulate and inspire.

The centennial anniversary of the birth of this great

American physicist was marked by another dedication in 1952. It took place at the border of the two campuses of the Case Institute and Western Reserve University in Cleveland. Ceremonies commemorating the famous Michelson-Morley experiment were conducted by the Cleveland Physics Society. A plaque bears this inscription:

> *Near this spot, in July 1887, Dr. A. A. Michelson of Case and Dr. E. W. Morley of Western Reserve conducted the world-famous Michelson-Morley Experiment, one of the outstanding scientific achievements of the nineteenth century and a cornerstone of modern physics. In commemoration this tablet has been set in stone by both colleges on the 100th anniversary of Dr. Michelson's birth.*
> Dec. 19, 1952.

APPENDIX I

The More Important of the 78 Papers of Michelson

1. On a Method of Measuring the Velocity of Light, *Am. J. Sci.*, Vol. 15, 394–95. 1878
2. Experimental Determination of the Velocity of Light, *Proc. AAAS*, Vol. 27, 71–77. 1878
3. Experimental Determination of the Velocity of Light, *Am. J. Sci.*, Series 3, Vol. 18, 390–93. 1879
4. Experimental Determination of the Velocity of Light, U. S. Nautical Almanac Office, *Astronomical Papers 1*, Part III, 115–45. 1880
5. The Relative Motion of the Earth and the Luminiferous Ether, *Am. J. Sci.*, Series 3, Vol. 22, 120–29. 1881
6. On the Velocity of Light in CS_2 and the Difference in Velocity of Red and Blue Light in the Same, *Report of Brit. AAS*, 654. 1884
7. Influence of Motion of the Medium on the Velocity of Light (with Morley), *Am. J. Sci.*, Series 3, Vol. 31, 377–86. 1886

8. On the Relative Motion of the Earth and the Luminiferous Ether (with Morley), *Am. J. Sci.*, Series 3, Vol. 34, 333–45. 1887
9. On a Method of Making the Wave Length of Sodium Light the Actual and Practical Standard of Length (with Morley), *Am. J. Sci.*, Vol. 34, 427–30. 1887
10. On the Feasibility of Establishing a Light Wave as the Ultimate Standard of Length (with Morley), *Am. J. Sci.*, Series 3, Vol. 38, 181–86. 1889
11. On the Application of Interference Methods to Astronomical Measurements, *Phil. Mag.*, Vol. 30, 1–21. 1890
12. Measurement of Jupiter's Satellites by Interference, *Nature*, Vol. 45, 160–65. 1891
13. Comparison of the International Meter with the Wave Length of the Light of Cadmium, *Astron. and Astrophysics*, Vol. 12, 556–60. 1893
14. On the Broadening of Spectral Lines, *Astrophys. J.*, Vol. 2, 251–63. 1895
15. A Theory of the X-Rays, *Am. J. Sci.*, Vol. 1, 312–14. 1896
16. Source of X-Rays (with Stratton), *Science*, N.S. 3, 694–96. 1896
17. On the Relative Motion of the Earth and the Ether, *Am. J. Sci.*, Vol. 3, 475–78. 1897
18. Radiation in a Magnetic Field, *Astrophys. J.*, Vol. 6, 48–54. 1897
19. The Echelon Spectroscope, *Astrophys. J.*, Vol. 8, 37–47. 1898

20. A New Harmonic Analyzer (with Stratton), *Am. J. Sci.*, Vol. 5, 1–13. 1898
21. Relative Motion of Earth and Ether, *Phil. Mag.*, Vol. 8, 716–19. 1904
22. Report of Progress in Ruling Diffraction Gratings, *Phys. Rev.*, Vol. 20, 289. 1905
23. Form Analysis, *Proc. Am. Phil. Soc.*, Vol. 45, 110–16. 1906
24. Recent Advances in Spectroscopy, Nobel Address, Royal Academy of Science, Stockholm. 1907
25. On Metallic Coloring in Birds and Insects, *Phil. Mag.* Vol. 21, 554–67. 1911
26. Preliminary Results of Measurements of the Rigidity of the Earth, *Astrophys. J.*, Vol. 39, 105–38. 1914
27. The Ruling and Performance of a Ten-Inch Diffraction Grating, *Proc. Am. Phil. Soc.*, Vol. 54, 137–42. 1915
28. The Rigidity of the Earth (with Gale), *Astrophys. J.*, Vol. 50, 330–45. 1919
29. The Vertical Interferometer, *Proc. Nat'l Acad. of Sci.*, Vol. 6, 473–75. 1920
30. Measurement of the Diameter of Alpha Orionis with the Interferometer (with Pease), *Astrophys. J.*, Vol. 53, 249–59. 1921
31. Preliminary Experiments on the Velocity of Light, *Astrophys. J.*, Vol. 60, 256–61. 1924
32. The Effect of the Earth's Rotation on the Velocity of Light (with Gale), *Astrophys. J.*, Vol. 61, 137–45. 1925
33. Measurement of the Velocity of Light Be-

tween Mt. Wilson and Mt. San Antonio, *Astrophys. J.*, Vol. 65, 1–22. 1927

34. Repetition of the Michelson-Morley Experiment (with Pease and Pearson), *Nature*, Vol. 123, 88, Jan. 19, 1929. 1929
35. Measurement of the Velocity of Light in a Partial Vacuum (with Pease and Pearson), *Astrophys. J.*, Vol. 82, 26–61. 1935

Books by Michelson

1. *Light Waves and Their Uses*, 1903, University of Chicago Press (The Lowell Lectures of 1899).
2. *Studies in Optics*, 1927, University of Chicago Press.

APPENDIX II

Acknowledgments

The preparation of this book was made more enjoyable and much easier by the generous help of many people, including members of Dr. Michelson's family, his colleagues, students, and friends. Here is a partial list of these individuals.

Mr. Tilton M. Barron, Librarian, Clark University, Worcester, Massachusetts

Mr. Preston R. Bassett, Ridgefield, Connecticut

Mrs. Clara S. Beatty, Director, Nevada Historical Society, Reno, Nevada

Mrs. Festus Foster (Beatrice Michelson)

Mr. Ralph Friedman, Santa Monica, California

Captain Robert A. Hinners, Webb Institute of Naval Architecture, Glen Cove, New York

Mr. John Howe, Encyclopædia Britannica, New York City

Mr. Elbert L. Huber, Archivist in Charge, Navy Branch, National Archives, Washington, D.C.

Mr. Edward Lasker, New York City

Dr. Horace C. Levinson, Kennebunk, Maine

Mr. D. T. McAllister, Technical Information Department, U. S. Naval Ordnance Test Station, China Lake, California

Mr. George Mann, Director of Public Relations, Case Institute of Technology, Cleveland, Ohio

Mrs. Paul A. Meeres (Elsa Michelson)

Mrs. Frederick Mueller (Madeleine Michelson)

Mr. Allan R. Ottley, Librarian, California State Library, Sacramento, California

Dr. William B. Plum, U. S. Naval Civil Engineering Laboratory, Port Hueneme, California

Dr. Nathan Reingold, Science Bibliographer, Library of Congress, Washington, D.C.

Mr. Robert Rosenthal, Curator, Special Collections, University of Chicago Library, Chicago, Illinois

Professor John R. Smithson, U. S. Naval Academy, Annapolis, Maryland

Professor Vernon D. Tate, Librarian, U. S. Naval Academy, Annapolis, Maryland

Dr. Howard R. Williams, Akron, Ohio

Mr. H. R. Young, College Archivist, Case Institute of Technology, Cleveland, Ohio

My thanks to all of them, and also to John H. Durston, General Editor of Educational Services Incorporated, and to Miss Galina Terr, who, for the fourth time, took up another of my manuscripts and helped work it into final shape.

BERNARD JAFFE

Sources and Bibliography

Articles

1. "Albert A. Michelson," by Harvey B. Lemon, *The American Physics Teacher*, Vol. 4, No. 1, pp. 1–11, Feb. 1936.
2. "Albert A. Michelson," by Robert A. Millikan, *The Scientific Monthly*, Vol. 48, pp. 16–27, Jan. 1939.
3. "Michelson at Annapolis," by J. R. Smithson, *American Journal of Physics*, Vol. 18, No. 7, pp. 425–28, Oct. 1950.
4. "A. A. Michelson at Case," by R. S. Shankland, *American Journal of Physics*, Vol. 17, No. 8, pp. 487–90, Nov. 1949.
5. "Putting the Stars in Place," by Harold D. Carew, *Touring Topics*, pp. 24–26, 39, Sept. 1930.
6. "A. A. Michelson," by F. E. Beach, *American Journal of Science*, Aug. 1931.
7. "Michelson," by F. R. Moulton, *Popular Astronomy*, Vol. 39, No. 6, June–July 1931.
8. "Michelson," by Henry G. Gale, *Astrophysical Journal*, Vol. 74, pp. 1–9, July 1931.
9. "Some of Michelson's Researches," by G. E. Hale, *Astronomical Society of the Pacific*, Vol. 43, pp. 175–84, 1931.
10. "Obituary of Michelson," by F. Twyman, *Physical Society of London*, Vol. 40, pp. 625–32, Jan.–Sept. 1931.
11. "Nobel Prize Winners in Physics," by A. H. Compton, *Current History*, Aug. 1931.
12. "Duddell Medal Award," *Journal of Scientific Instruments*, London, April 1930.
13. "Michelson Meeting of Optical Society," *Journal of Optical Society of America*, Vol. 18, pp. 143–92, March 1929.

14. "Scientific Worthies," by Oliver Lodge, *Nature,* Vol. 117, pp. 1–6, Jan.–June 1926.
15. "Recent Progress in Spectroscopic Methods," by Michelson, *Nature,* Jan. 11, 1912.
16. "The Michelson Museum," by William B. Plum, *American Journal of Physics,* Vol. 22, No. 4, pp. 177–81, April 1954.

Books

1. *Mainstream of Mathematics,* by Edna E. Kramer, Oxford University Press, 1951.
2. *ABC of Relativity,* by Bertrand Russell, New American Library, 1958.
3. *The Universe and Dr. Einstein,* by Lincoln Barnett, Wm. Sloane Associates, 1948.
4. *Two New Worlds,* by Galileo Galilei, Dover Publications, 1959.
5. *Opticks,* by Isaac Newton, Dover Publications, 1952.
6. *Edward W. Morley,* by H. R. Williams, Chemical Education Publishing Co., 1957.
7. *One, Two, Three—Infinity,* by George Gamow, New American Library, 1953.
8. *From Galileo to Cosmic Rays,* by Harvey B. Lemon, University of Chicago Press, 1934.
9. *Roemer and the First Determination of the Velocity of Light,* by I. B. Cohen, The Burndy Library, 1942.
10. *From Midshipman to Rear Admiral,* by Bradley A. Fiske, Century, 1919.
11. *Men of Science in America,* by Bernard Jaffe, Simon and Schuster, 1958.
12. *Physics,* Vol. 2, prepared by the Physical Science Study Committee, Massachusetts Institute of Technology, 1958.
13. *A Hundred Years of Physics,* by William Wilson, Duckworth & Co., London, 1950.

Index

SCIENCE STUDY SERIES

ANDRADE, E. N. da C. *Rutherford and the Nature of the Atom,* S35

—— *Sir Isaac Newton—His Life and Work,* S42

ASIMOV, ISAAC *A Short History of Chemistry,* S41

BASCOM, WILLARD *Waves and Beaches: The Dynamics of the Ocean Surface,* S34

BATTAN, LOUIS J. *The Nature of Violent Storms,* S19
Radar Observes the Weather, S24
Cloud Physics and Cloud Seeding, S29

BENADE, ARTHUR H. *Horns, Strings & Harmony,* S11

BITTER, FRANCIS *Magnets: The Education of a Physicist,* S2

—— *Mathematical Aspects of Physics: An Introduction,* S32

BONDI, HERMANN *Relativity and Common Sense,* S36

—— *The Universe at Large,* S14

BOYS, SIR CHARLES VERNON *Soap Bubbles and the Forces Which Mould Them,* S3

BROWN, SANBORN C. *Count Rumford,* S28

COHEN, I. BERNARD *The Birth of a New Physics,* S10

DAVIS, KENNETH S., & DAY, JOHN ARTHUR *Water: The Mirror of Science,* S18

DUBOS, RENE *Pasteur and Modern Science,* S15

FINK, DONALD G., & LUTYENS, DAVID M. *The Physics of Television,* S8

GALAMBOS, ROBERT *Nerves and Muscles,* S25

GAMOW, GEORGE *Gravity,* S22

GRIFFIN, DONALD R. *Bird Migration,* S37

—— *Echoes of Bats and Men,* S4

HOLDEN, ALAN, & SINGER, PHYLIS *Crystals and Crystal Growing,* S7

HUGHES, DONALD J. *The Neutron Story,* S1

HURLEY, PATRICK M. *How Old Is the Earth?* S5

JAFFE, BERNARD *Michelson and the Speed of Light,* S13

KOCK, WINSTON E. *Sound Waves and Light Waves,* S40

KOESTLER, ARTHUR *The Watershed: A Biography of Johannes Kepler,* S16

LITTAUER, RAPHAEL, & WILSON, ROBERT R. *Accelerators: Machines of Nuclear Physics,* S17

MAC DONALD, D. K. C. *Faraday, Maxwell, and Klevin,* S33

—— *Near Zero: The Physics of Low Temperature,* S20

OVENDEN, MICHAEL W. *Life in the Universe,* S23

PAGE, ROBERT MORRIS *The Origin of Radar,* S26

PIERCE, JOHN R. *Electrons and Waves,* S38

ROMER, ALFRED *The Restless Atom,* S12

SANDFORT, JOHN F. *Heat Engines,* S27

SHAPIRO, ASCHER H. *Shape and Flow: The Fluid Dynamics of Drag,* S21

STEWART, ALEC T. *Perpetual Motion: Electrons and Crystals in Atoms,* S39

VAN BERGEIJK, WILLEM A.; PIERCE, JOHN R.; & DAVID, EDWARD E., JR. *Waves and the Ear,* S9

WEAVER, WARREN *Lady Luck: The Theory of Probability,* S30

WEISSKOPF, VICTOR F. *Knowledge and Wonder: The Natural World as Man Knows It,* S31